DISCARD

QA75.
4.P3
1966

Paul, Robert John Alexander
Fundamental analogue
techniques

D1248109

FUNDAMENTAL ANALOGUE TECHNIQUES

FUNDAMENTAL ANALOGUE TECHNIQUES

Professor R. J. A. PAUL

School of Engineering Science
University College of North Wales

THE MACMILLAN COMPANY, NEW YORK

THE MACMILLAN COMPANY
60 Fifth Avenue
New York 11, N.Y.

©
R. J. A. PAUL
1965
First published in U.S.A. 1966

Library of Congress Catalog Card No. 66–15928

Printed in Great Britain by Blackie & Son Limited, Glasgow

AUTHOR'S PREFACE

ANALOGUE COMPUTING DEVICES AND, IN PARTICULAR, THE electronic analogue computer are everyday tools of the modern applied scientist and engineer. For effective use of these tools it is necessary to have an appreciation of the fundamental principles involved, and it is hoped that this book will fulfill this need.

In a book of this size it is necessary to restrict the subject matter and this is confined to techniques and basic principles rather than to detailed descriptions of various devices.

Chapter 1 forms an introduction to computing aids and indicates that analogue computing techniques should be regarded as complementary to digital techniques rather than as possible rivals. The second chapter is devoted to a general treatment of the basic principles of the differential analyser leading to a more detailed treatment of the electronic machine. The preparation of problems and the operation of the analogue computer to solve these problems is described in chapter 3. Dynamic analogies and the construction of analogous networks forms the subject matter of chapter 4. The inclusion of this chapter should aid the reader to appreciate some simple generalized dynamic concepts which are used in the construction of mathematical descriptions of discrete (lumped) parameter systems. Chapter 5 describes the iterative operation of the analogue computer using asynchronous mode control as opposed to the usual synchronous mode control described in the earlier chapters. The final chapter is concerned with the simulation of rational transfer functions, since this approach for particular applications has many advantages compared with the differential equation representation of dynamic systems.

The author is painfully aware of many omissions in subject matter, but has attempted to treat in sufficient detail a limited coverage rather than a superficial treatment of a wider field of techniques and applications. In this way it is hoped that the text will help the interested reader to pursue paths of more specialized aspect. These include the solution of partial differential equations, hybrid analogue/digital techniques, the treatment of stochastic systems and optimum search procedures involved in the study of dynamic systems. On the equipment side there are adequate references

v

AUTHOR'S PREFACE

concerned with detailed circuit configurations of amplifiers, function generators, multipliers, logic elements and other devices which form the complement of a modern analogue machine.

In preparing the draft the author would like to acknowledge the helpful advice given to him by his former colleagues at the College of Aeronautics, Cranfield. In particular, he wishes to thank Mr. S. R. Deards for reading chapters 1, 2 and 6 and for his constructive criticism of the text. Thanks are also due to him for his suggestion of the use of symmetrical lattice network reduction in the synthesis procedure described in section 6.5 of chapter 6 and for the use of the unpublished lecture supplements referenced in chapter 4. The author also acknowledges the help of Mr. A. J. Martin in reading chapters 3, 4 and 5 and his suggested amendments. The experimental results given in chapter 5 are also due to Mr. Martin.

Finally, grateful thanks are due to Mrs. M. Jewell and Mrs. H. Laurie-Lean for typing the manuscript and to Miss Diane Sargent for tracing the diagrams.

R. J. A. PAUL

5th May 1965

vi

EDITOR'S PREFACE

THE INVENTION OF THE TRANSISTOR AND THE VARIETY OF semiconductor devices, the growth of electronic computers, both analogue and digital, and the increasing use of electronic apparatus for measurement and for control are examples of the rapid development of electronics, which has caused the penetration of these devices into an ever-widening range of application. In big business, in banking and accountancy, in medicine and manufacturing, in textile and chemical industries, the use of electronics has become commonplace. In science, electronics has revolutionized research technique from radioastronomy to the electron microscope. One result is a demand for knowledge by the users of this bewildering array of electronic apparatus now available. The new 'Electronic User Series' is designed for this purpose and is intended for qualified scientists and engineers for whom electronics is a fringe activity.

It is a series in which later volumes depend to some extent on the first two volumes. These two books, *Electronic Devices and Networks* and *Electronic Circuit Techniques* by Professor E. E. Zepler and Mr. S. W. Punnett, are intended to cover the basic electronic requirements (excluding communications) and to form an introduction to the more specialized topics of the rest of the series. This eliminates the undue repetition of elementary principles and allows comprehensive coverage in texts of moderate size.

The authors are all recognized experts in their own specialized fields and the selection of the subjects has been made by considering only those areas in which there is, or has been recently, rapid development. Because of the general advancement of electronics this has not imposed a severe restriction, and the final choice of topics has been somewhat difficult.

The books of this series are not primarily aimed at electrical engineering students and do not cover any particular syllabus or examination; nevertheless it is hoped that the series will be of use to both student and lecturer.

JOHN C. WEST

University of Belfast
26th October, 1962

CONTENTS

Chapter 1

INTRODUCTION

1.1 THE NEED FOR COMPUTING AIDS

FROM THE EARLIEST TIMES, THE USE OF COMPUTING AIDS HAS resulted in significant advances in man's thought process with beneficial results to the general environment.

Initially the standard of living of primitive communities was largely determined by the human muscular power available. Simple machine aids were gradually evolved and a most significant advance was the invention of the wheel. Wind and water power were harnessed to some extent to suit man's needs, and animal power was also used.

The need for communication and recording of events resulted at first in the symbolic representation of events and numbers by piles of stones, and this led to the development of crude drawings, the concept of symbols, and eventually to a written language. To aid in counting numbers and events the abacus (bead counting) was invented and in many countries this is still used today.

However, until the industrial revolution the major contributions to the general living conditions were still derived from human muscular power, although helped to some extent by simple machine aids (such as the counting machine, slide rule and planimeter), and animal, wind and water power. With the industrial era, human power was replaced in many applications by other forms of power such as steam and electricity. Progress was now determined by the ability of man to control this power and to use it effectively. In other words, the major advances in living conditions were determined by the amount of logical thought available to conceive machines to use this power. The design of such machines gradually showed the need for more effective computing aids, and this led to the development of the desk calculating machine.

Despite the tremendous advances in scientific thought and technological progress from that time to the present day, it is only within the past few decades that the desk calculating machine in its various forms has been replaced, for some applications, by faster and more effective computing aids.

The rapid increase in scientific applications evolved during World War II proved the need for more effective and faster methods of performing

1

numerous protracted calculations involved in the design of equipment and systems. Another need arose in the requirement for a mathematical model to represent the performance of a system or combination of devices, so that the designer could acquire knowledge of the behaviour and the physical limitations imposed in the system. In many applications a graphical solution is preferred to discrete solutions of arithmetical operations, as the physical behaviour of the system represented is more easily interpreted from the graphical solution. Moreover, in many applications, it is not possible to produce an exact mathematical representation of each device and an approximate functional graphical relationship is then used. In this type of problem the graphical solution in the first instance may not be required to a high degree of accuracy, as the main aim initially is to understand the physical performance and interaction of components of the system. The graphical study may lead to a better understanding of the system and this may result in a more exact representation.

The types of problem which have evolved and of course are still with us today may be put into the following broad categories:

(i) Fast and accurate solution of arithmetical operations (i.e. addition, subtraction, multiplication, etc.) or, putting it crudely: doing sums.

(ii) The representation of the behaviour of a device or devices by a mathematical model as a means of understanding the physical processes involved in the equipment.

(iii) Solution of algebraic and differential equations which represent the behaviour of the physical devices.

These problems have resulted in two main types of computing aids: the electronic digital computer and the electronic analogue computer.

The modern digital computer is essentially an automatic device capable of performing addition and subtraction in simple discrete steps (digits) to as high a degree of accuracy as required. The analogue computer on the other hand presents a graphical solution of equations within a limited degree of accuracy; in other words it draws a graph and operates continuously in time.

According to Chambers's Dictionary the modern meaning of computer is defined as: 'a calculator; a large machine carrying out calculations of several stages automatically'.

In this text, this modern definition is implied when the word 'computer' is used and manually operated aids such as desk calculators, slide rules, etc. are referred to as computing aids or calculating instruments.

The word 'digit' is derived from the Latin word 'digitus' meaning a finger or a toe. For scientific application the word 'digit' may be defined as a figure used in arithmetic to represent a number. An electronic digital computer, therefore, is an automatic calculator using digits to represent numbers, with the specific interpretation of 'digit' as a discrete bit of information represented by the presence or absence of an electrical impulse in a chain of impulses.

The word 'analogy' may be defined as 'an agreement or correspondence in certain respects between things otherwise different'. The scientific interpretation is that the physical behaviour of a certain device or assembly of devices may be represented by the performance of other devices of different physical form, provided that the mathematical relationships defining the physical behaviour in the two cases are identical.

Thus an analogous system is one representing another system of different physical form, the correspondence between the two systems being defined by the mathematical relationships involved.

An analogue computer may be defined as an automatic means for representing the performance of a physical system by solving the mathematical equations or relationships defining the behaviour of the system in a continuous manner. However, modern usage implies that an electronic analogue computer is a machine comprising several discrete computing units, such as integrating units, adding units, multiplying units, etc. in which the mathematical operations are performed in a continuous manner. In other words, the modern implication is that the machine is in fact a *Differential Analyser*; a device capable of solving differential and algebraic equations.

1.2 SOME COMPARISONS BETWEEN DIGITAL AND ANALOGUE COMPUTERS

1.2.1 Modes of Operation

The main difference between the analogue and digital computer lies in the mode of operation. Since the digital computer operates in discrete steps, and processes bits (digits) of information, it can be made as accurate as required because, theoretically, there is no limit on the number of digits representing a number or quantity. All mathematical operations on a digital machine are based on its ability to add and subtract a series of digits representing the problem variables.

The basic unit of one form of analogue computer (the differential analyser) is the integrator which is a device capable of integrating one or more input variables with respect to an independent variable. This computing unit, as well as other units such as the adder, multiplier, etc. operates continuously with respect to the independent variable which may be time or some function of time. This continuous representation of problem variables, which may be in the form of shaft rotation in a mechanical machine or a voltage in an electronic machine, limits the accuracy which may be obtained. Once the computation is started, time dependent errors increase as the computing proceeds. Moreover, the instrumentation of the mathematical operations of integration, addition, etc. are based on the use of physical devices which can only be made to a limited degree of accuracy.

Thus we may say that the digital machine is an automatic device for performing arithmetical operations with digits which represent the problem variables to any desired degree of accuracy, whereas problem variables in the analogue computer are represented in a continuous manner in some physical form, such as mechanical displacement or voltage, to a limited degree of accuracy.

1.2.2 The Digital Computer

Historical Note

The concept of the automatic digital computer is not new and is due to Charles Babbage who was Professor of Mathematics at Cambridge University, 1828–39.[1] Babbage proposed the essential elements of the modern machine as early as 1835 but the practical realization of his ideas was confined to mechanical components which were somewhat unreliable and slow in operation.

The first large automatic digital machine actually built was the I.B.M. Automatic Sequenced Controlled Calculator developed by Professor H. Aitken and the I.B.M. Company at Harvard University and completed in 1944. This computer combined mechanical, electrical and electro-mechanical elements and was very slow in operation by present standards. The first electronic computer was the E.N.I.A.C. (1947) followed by the I.B.M. Electronic Calculator in 1948. In England these were followed by the Cambridge University E.D.S.A.C. computer, the National Physical Laboratory A.C.E. computer and the Manchester University Ferranti Mark I computer.

From these early machines stems the whole family of modern computers.

Basic Operations

The modern computer is essentially an automatic device capable of performing four basic operations: addition, subtraction, memorization and discrimination.

It may also be programmed to multiply and divide but these are not basic operations and are carried out by repeated addition and subtraction respectively. For example if we wish to multiply 17 by 5 we may obtain the result by adding together five seventeens. Again to divide 54 by 6, we get the result by subtracting 6 from 54 to give 48, subtracting 6 from 48 to give 42 and so on until the remainder is less than 6 or zero. The number of times the number 6 has been subtracted is the quotient.

The computer operates with digit numbers represented by electrical pulses and these are counted in a similar manner to the beads on a child's counter. It cannot perform mathematical operations beyond the scope of a human brain and can in fact only give answers to specific questions. Its usefulness lies in its extremely high computational speed in relation to that of a human operator, who would take a lifetime to perform the routine arithmetical operations which the machine could perform in a few days.

Any mathematical operation can be performed by a very large number of arithmetical operations. This procedure is too tedious for a human operator, who would prefer to use (if applicable) more elegant mathematical procedures. However, because of the speed of operation in the electronic computer, the time involved in performing the large number of arithmetical operations is relatively short.

As the machine is only capable of performing the four basic operations already mentioned, the problem to be solved must be split into very detailed operations before being fed into the machine. This procedure is called *programming* and essentially asks the machine to operate as follows:

(*a*) Perform a series of arithmetical operations until a certain stage is reached.

(*b*) Change method and perform a different series of operations.

(*c*) Repeat until the complete series of operations is performed to required accuracy.

The various stages are often not recognizable until they are reached during the computation, so the computer must be able to discriminate. For example the discrimination might be: 'Change to operation B when the number resulting from operation A is less than a certain value'. Again a numerical solution usually involves many separate calculations, saving the individual answers and then combining them at some later stage of the solution; the computer must therefore be capable of memorizing numbers and instructions.

Number Representation

The Decimal System

The decimal code 0 to 9 is used in everyday life because man presumably first learned to count with his fingers. With this decimal code a digit has ten possible values to represent the numbers 0 to 9. Consider the number 965, or in words, nine hundred and sixty and five. The number really comprises five units + 6 lots of 10 units + 9 lots of 10 parcels of 10 units. In this system of counting the number 10 thus has a special significance in that each digit in a particular number represents a value given by the digit multiplied by 10 raised to a certain power. Thus 965 is equivalent to $(9 \times 10^2) + (6 \times 10^1) + (5 \times 10^0)$.

The Binary Code

If man had first used his hands to count instead of his fingers, a binary system or code, more simple than a decimal one, would have evolved. Only two symbols 0 and 1 are needed to represent a digit in this system. Since devices having only two states, i.e. 'off' and 'on', are more easily produced than those having ten possible states, the binary system is used almost exclusively in modern computers. The input data to the machine are generally in decimal code because we are more familiar with it and the machine converts it into binary code. The output data are converted by the machine from binary into decimal code.

In the binary system the number 2 has the same significance as 10 in the decimal system. In other words each digit in a number represents 2 raised to some power.

In both binary and decimal codes zero is represented by 0 and unity by 1.

To convert the decimal number 965 to binary code we divide by 2 repeatedly as follows:

$$
\begin{array}{r|l}
2 & 965 \\
2 & 482 \text{ and remainder } 1 \\
2 & 241 \text{ and remainder } 0 \\
2 & 120 \text{ and remainder } 1 \\
2 & 60 \text{ and remainder } 0 \\
2 & 30 \text{ and remainder } 0 \\
2 & 15 \text{ and remainder } 0 \\
2 & 7 \text{ and remainder } 1 \\
2 & 3 \text{ and remainder } 1 \\
2 & 1 \text{ and remainder } 1 \\
2 & 0 \text{ and remainder } 1 \\
\end{array}
$$

The answer and remainder after first division consists of 482 lots of 2 and 1 unit. At the next stage it consists of 241 parcels of 2 units of 2, 0 parcels of 2 and 1 unit. Repeating this procedure until the division is complete we find the digits of the binary number representing 965.

Thus decimal 965 is represented in the binary code by

$$1 \; 1 \; 1 \; 1 \; 0 \; 0 \; 0 \; 1 \; 0 \; 1 \quad \text{represented in Fig. 1.1}$$

Fig. 1.1 *Pulse train representing binary number* 1 1 1 1 0 0 0 1 0 1

To convert the binary number to decimal code we reverse the process as follows:

$$1 \; 1 \; 1 \; 1 \; 0 \; 0 \; 0 \; 1 \; 0 \; 1 \equiv (1 \times 2^0) + (0 \times 2^1) + (1 \times 2^2) + (0 \times 2^3) + (0 \times 2^4)$$

$$= 1 \quad = 0 \quad = 4 \quad = 0 \quad = 0$$

$$+ (0 \times 2^5) + (1 \times 2^6) + (1 \times 2^7) + (1 \times 2^8) + (1 \times 2^9)$$

$$= 0 \quad = 64 \quad = 128 \quad = 256 \quad = 512$$

$$= 1 + 4 + 64 + 128 + 256 + 512$$

$$= 965 \text{ (decimal)}$$

For further information, the reader is referred to Reference 2 which is a simple introduction to digital computers.

1.2.3 The Analogue Computer

Basic Mode of Operation

In the analogue machine numbers are represented by some physical quantity such as angular rotation, length, temperature or voltage. In other words it is not a counting machine like the digital but rather a measuring machine.

Let us consider two simple examples to illustrate this point.

(*i*) Suppose we wish to add two numbers N_1 and N_2

i.e.
$$N = N_1 + N_2 \tag{1.1}$$

e.g. if $N_1 = 5\cdot6$ and $N_2 = 10\cdot9$, we may represent these numbers by angular rotations θ_1 and θ_2

where
$$\theta_1 = a_\theta \times 5\cdot6$$

and
$$\theta_2 = a_\theta \times 10\cdot9$$
$$(1.2)$$

where θ_1 and θ_2 are expressed in degrees and a_θ is an amplitude scale factor expressed in degrees per unit number. The instrumentation of this

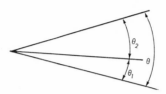

Fig. 1.2 *Measurement of angular displacement*

simple calculation may be achieved by means of a protractor as illustrated in Fig. 1.2. The sum θ is obtained by measurement of the addition of the two angles

where
$$\theta = a_\theta N$$

so that the desired result is given by

$$N = \frac{\theta}{a_\theta} \qquad (1.3)$$

(*ii*) The simple slide rule

Suppose we wish to multiply two numbers N_1 and N_2

so that
$$N = N_1 N_2 \qquad (1.4)$$

we may perform this calculation by means of logarithms.

Thus
$$\log_{10} N = \log_{10} N_1 + \log_{10} N_2 \qquad (1.5)$$

We may instrument this procedure by representing the logarithm of the numbers by lengths.

Thus if
$$L_1 = a_L \log_{10} N_1$$
$$L_2 = a_L \log_{10} N_2$$
$$L = a_L \log_{10} N$$
$$(1.6)$$

where a_L is a scale factor expressed as length on a $\log_{10}$ scale.

Then
$$L = L_1 + L_2 \qquad (1.7)$$

This is of course the principle of the slide rule as illustrated in Fig. 1.3.

The method used to multiply 4 by 2 is illustrated. The 1 on the cursor is positioned to coincide with 4 on the fixed lower scale. The number given on the latter which coincides with the multiplying number, in this case 2, is the required result which in this case is 8.

It is apparent that the accuracy of performing these two simple operations is limited as it is dependent on the accuracy of measurement, which in turn is related to the scale factor chosen. These elementary computing aids deal with constant input data. The analogue computer, however, is capable of accepting input functions which vary with time, as distinct from constant numbers, and performing in a continuous manner the basic mathematical operations of addition, subtraction, multiplication and integration, in addition to the generation of arbitrary functions of variables. Usually, in a

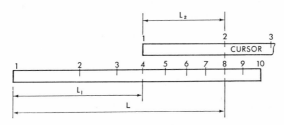

Fig. 1.3 *Number represented by length on a $\log_{10}$ scale*

general purpose machine, each type of mathematical operation is performed by a separate computing unit and arrangements are provided so that these may be interconnected in an easy and flexible manner to solve a wide variety of problems.

In practice the instrumentation of the mathematical operations is based on mechanical, electromechanical, electrical or electronic methods. The precision, or number of significant figures representing a variable, is dependent on the accuracy of the computer components and the output measuring equipment.

One important feature of the analogue machine is that all computing units operate simultaneously, i.e. parallel operation, thus providing the solution almost immediately. This facility is a considerable advantage to the operator as it permits him to investigate the effect of varying design parameters and thus to gain a physical insight into the behaviour of the system under investigation.

The digital computer can only give specific answers to specific questions put to it and because of the lack of knowledge of the physical behaviour of the system being studied, the difficulty in many studies is to find the right questions. In such studies the analogue computer may be used, to advantage, to obtain a better understanding of behaviour and to assess initial conditions by the logical interpretation of the graphical results.

In applications requiring high accuracy of solution, this procedure leads to a more intelligent and economic use of the digital machine since the number of questions set to the machine is considerably reduced. Moreover, the analogue study may lead to a more exact mathematical model and thus a better understanding of the physical processes involved.

Types of Analogue Computer

Analogue devices may be classified according to the application, the basic principle of operation, and the physical form of the computer components.

A special purpose computer is one designed to solve a specific problem and generally would not be easily adapted to other types of problem.

A general purpose computer is capable of solving a wide variety of problems and is so designed that interconnections of computing units may be achieved in a flexible and easy manner. Facilities are usually provided for the incorporation of extra units or the replacement of one type of unit by another.

Direct and Indirect Representation

The method of solution may be based on a direct or indirect analogy.

Direct Representation

Direct computers are known as direct simulators. Here the physical system under investigation is represented in the simulator by an analogous system, every element of which corresponds in a mathematical sense to the corresponding element of the real system. In other words, the mathematical

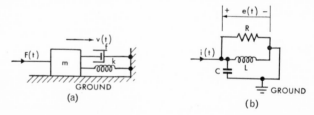

Fig. 1.4 (a) *Mechanical network*   (b) *Analogous electrical network*

relationship between excitation and response of each element in the two systems is identical. Moreover the analogous elements in the computer are interconnected in the same way as the physical system, i.e. the topology of each system is identical.

The physical system may be represented by continuous or lumped (discrete) physical elements, and in this case the analogous system will also comprise continuous or discrete elements.

To illustrate this point, let us consider an analogous electrical system to represent the performance of the simple discrete parameter mechanical network shown in Fig. 1.4.

All components are assumed to be ideal and linear. It is assumed that the mass m moves on a smooth surface with zero friction.

$F(t)$ is the force applied with respect to ground
$v(t)$ is the velocity of mass with respect to ground
f is the viscous friction coefficient of a dash pot
k is the spring constant of a linear spring
$i(t)$ is the current flowing into the electrical network
$e(t)$ is the potential difference across the network
R is the resistance value of a resistor
L is the inductance value of an inductor
C is the capacitance value of a capacitor.

For network (a) we have, assuming the spring is relaxed initially

$$F(t) = F_m + F_f + F_k \qquad (1.8)$$

where F_m = force to accelerate mass = $m\dfrac{dv(t)}{dt}$

F_f = force to overcome viscous friction = fv

F_k = force to contract the spring = $k\displaystyle\int_{0+}^{t} v\,dt$

Thus $\qquad F(t) = m\dfrac{dv(t)}{dt} + fv(t) + k\displaystyle\int_{0+}^{t} v(t)\,dt \qquad (1.9)$

For network (b), assuming the inductor is relaxed initially

$$i(t) = i_R + i_L + i_C \qquad (1.10)$$

where i_R = current flowing through the resistor branch = $\dfrac{e(t)}{R}$

i_L = current flowing through inductor branch = $\dfrac{1}{L}\displaystyle\int_{0+}^{t} e(t)\,dt$

i_C = current flowing through capacitor branch = $C\dfrac{d}{dt}e(t)$

Thus
$$i(t) = C\frac{d}{dt}e(t) + \frac{1}{R}e(t) + \frac{1}{L}\int_{0+}^{t} e(t)\,dt \tag{1.11}$$

Comparing equations (1.9) and (1.11) we see that

$i(t)$ is analogous to $F(t)$

C is analogous to m

$\dfrac{1}{R}$ is analogous to f

$\dfrac{1}{L}$ is analogous to k

Therefore we may analyse the performance of network (a) by studying the performance of network (b) which may be more easily constructed.

Note: It is possible to derive a dual equivalent electrical network for (a), in which $i(t)$ is analogous to $v(t)$ and $e(t)$ analogous to $F(t)$, but this network is not topologically coincident with (a). (See Chapter 4.)

The analogous system above is based on the similarity of function relationships of each element. The mass m and spring k are reservoirs or stores of energy, as are C and L. Viscous friction coefficient f and resistor R cause dissipation of energy in the form of heat. We may note at this stage that the performance of lumped parameter systems is characterized by ordinary differential equations. In many applications this lumped parameter representation of a physical system is satisfactory, particularly if we are concerned with the behaviour of elements as a whole and are not concerned with what happens inside each element.

If, for instance, we are concerned with the behaviour of the spring throughout its length obviously it cannot be completely specified by the parameter k

i.e.
$$\frac{\text{displacement between extremities}}{\text{force through spring}}$$

Use of the parameter k implies that the force applied to one end of the spring is transmitted instantly, i.e. the spring has zero mass and frictional damping. Thus we see that lumping all the properties of the spring as the spring constant 'k' is an approximation, which may be valid if we are only concerned with the behaviour of the spring as an element in a network with other elements, in which the effect of spring mass and friction may be ignored.

The implied assumption of the lumped parameter network is that each element is characterized by a lumped parameter (i.e. a functional relationship between two quantities) and the spatial position and size of each element is of no significance. Moreover the lines interconnecting the discrete elements, which may be linkages in a mechanical system or connecting wires in an electrical circuit, also have no significance with regard to length or size, but only as an indication of how the elements are intercoupled.

Suppose now that we are interested in the internal behaviour of the spring. We must recognize the fact that the spring has distributed mass and friction along its relevant spatial co-ordinates. In other words the spring is characterized by continuous parameters which are functions of spatial co-ordinates. The spatial co-ordinates are additional independent variables to the one independent variable 'time' in the lumped parameter case.

The performance of a physical device represented by continuous parameters is characterized by partial differential equations, i.e. equations involving more than one independent variable and partial derivatives with respect to these variables. In the case of network (a) the internal behaviour of the coil spring is characterized by one extra independent space variable, i.e. length along the spring. Thus network (a) is a one-dimensional system.[3]

If, however, the spring constituted an elastic cylinder, we would have a three-dimensional system.

In general, the n-dimensional space within which an element is restrained to move may be regarded as a field.

Analogous systems for field problems are again based on the similarity of functional relationships of elements in different physical systems, i.e. energy reservoirs and energy dissipation elements. For example, in a two-dimensional heat transfer problem, where the sheet has finite dimensions and specified boundary conditions, the performance may be studied by our equivalent electrical analogue by the use of equivalent variables and parameters in two systems i.e.

Variables

    Current is analogous to Heat Flux
    Voltage is analogous to Temperature

Parameters

    Energy dissipation:
        Resistance is analogous to Thermal Resistance
        Capacitance is analogous to Thermal Capacity

Thus the direct electrical analogue comprises an electrical conducting sheet with specified voltages and currents applied to its edges, and having a resistance which varies in the relevant spatial co-ordinates in the same way as thermal resistance varies in the original system. Scale factors may be introduced to give suitable dimensions and parameter values in the analogous system.

Instruments used for the direct simulation of field problems include the electrolytic tank, the electrical conducting sheet (tele-deltos paper), etc.

(For a fuller description of these techniques and instruments see Reference 3.)

Indirect Representation

Computers in this category may be described as graphical equation solvers. The system under investigation is represented on the computer by the mathematical equations governing performance. For the lumped parameter system the equations involved will be algebraic or ordinary differential equations.

The analogue machine used for the solution of these equations is, as already described, the differential analyser with which this book is mainly concerned.

Such a machine may also be used as a servo or system simulator in which the transfer function (mathematical relationship between output and input) of each component block of the system is simulated, and the simulated blocks are interconnected in the computer in the same topological manner as the elements in the real system.[4] These component blocks may represent combinations of various lumped elements, e.g. mass, spring, transducers, resistors, capacitors, etc. If, therefore, each block is broken down so that each element is simulated, the differential analyser provides a direct simulation for continuous systems. As we have seen field problems lead to partial differential equations. Such equations may be solved to a limited degree of accuracy by finite difference techniques in which the field parameters are represented by a mesh or network of discrete parameters.

These approximate equations resulting from this approach may be solved on the differential analyser. An alternative approach is to use a network analyser which essentially provides a direct analogous system to the finite difference network representation of the mathematical model. (See Reference 3.)

A new type of computer has recently been introduced in an effort to obtain the combined advantages of analogue and digital techniques. This computer is the 'incremental' or so-called digital differential analyser (D.D.A.),[5] in which mathematical operations are computed digitally in discrete computing units. The latter, however, are interconnected in the same way as in the analogue differential analyser.

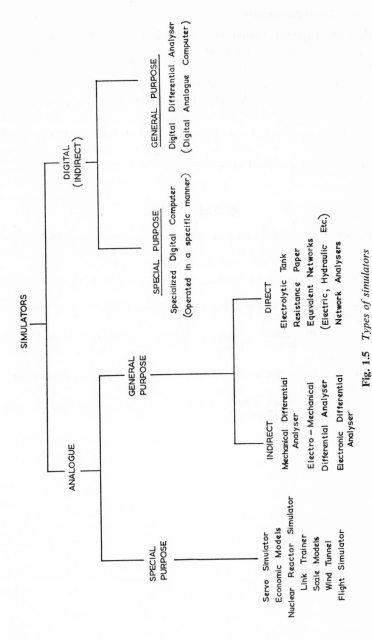

Fig. 1.5 *Types of simulators*

15

Classification of Simulators

A selection of typical simulators is shown in Fig. 1.5. It should be noted that the classification is not rigid and only a few examples under each heading are included.[6]

The special purpose devices will not be considered further in this text as their design is based on the same fundamental concepts as the general purpose machine. They are extremely useful for long term development projects or as training aids,[7] as they may be designed to perform specific tasks much more efficiently than their general purpose counterpart, although at the expense of versatility.

REFERENCES

1. D. R. HARTREE: *Calculating Instruments and Machines* (Cambridge University Press, 1949).

2. E. H. W. HERSEE: *A Simple Approach to Electronic Computers* (Blackie, 1959).

3. W. J. KARPLUS: *Analog Simulation* (*Solution of Field Problems*) (McGraw-Hill, 1958).

4. R. J. A. PAUL: 'Analogue Simulation in System Design' *Control*, 1958, **1**, pp. 221–6 and pp. 276–8.

5. R. J. A. PAUL and G. C. ROWLEY: 'Hybrid Computing Techniques', I.Mech.E. Symposium, *The use of Computers in Mechanical Engineering*, 1962, Paper 3, pp. 20–9.

6. R. J. A. PAUL: 'Review of Analogue Computing Techniques', *ibid.*, Paper 1, pp. 5–13.

7. J. J. FOODY and R. J. A. PAUL: 'Simulation Techniques in Aeronautics', *J. Roy. Aero. Soc.*, 1958, **62**, pp. 878–92.

Chapter 2

THE DIFFERENTIAL ANALYSER

2.1 HISTORICAL DEVELOPMENT

THE DIFFERENTIAL ANALYSER CONSISTS ESSENTIALLY OF A number of integrating devices which may be connected together to produce solutions of ordinary differential equations.

This basic concept was originally suggested by Lord Kelvin,[1,2] who in his first paper[1] discussed the use of two mechanical integrators, connected in the form of a closed loop, to solve second order linear differential equations. In his second paper[2] he extended the idea to linear equations of any order and in an addendum discussed the application to solutions of non-linear equations.

Although Kelvin's basic procedure is the same as that used today, it was not until 1931 that a practical machine based on these proposals was produced by Dr. Bush[3] and his colleagues at M.I.T. (Massachusetts Institute of Technology). This time lag was due mainly to lack of interest in the need for such a machine and difficulties in producing components to the required accuracy. A significant factor in the practical realization of the original conceptions of a machine was the invention of the torque amplifier by C. W. Nieman.[4] This device gave Bush the means to overcome the difficulties of coupling the various computing units in an effective and practical manner. The group under Dr. Bush started work at M.I.T. in 1925 and apparently developed their machine without any knowledge of Kelvin's earlier papers. This machine was followed in England with the installation of a four (later increased to eight) integrator machine[5,6,7] at the University of Manchester and a similar machine at the University of Cambridge in 1939. In the U.S.S.R. the differential analyser originated with the work of A. M. Krylov, during the period 1904–11,[18] who is reported to have built a machine with four integrators. In 1938 a mechanical analyser with six integrators was built. These early machines were primarily mechanical and used as the form of analogue representation (i) the angular position of a rotating shaft and (ii) distance. Connections between the various computing units (integrators, adders, multipliers, etc.) were achieved by coupling shafts and gears. With this method many man hours were involved in setting up a problem, and this fact led to the next

17

development which was the use of electrical servo-mechanisms to establish the connection between two mechanical units. By this means the mechanical interconnections were replaced by electrical interconnections. The first machine of this type was again built at M.I.T. by Bush and Caldwell.[8] This method resulted in a significant reduction of setting-up time and the machine could be programmed in a few hours instead of days. The computing units were basically unchanged in nature, but had improved performance with an integrator accuracy of about 1 part in 10,000. The earlier machines varied in performance, but a typical component accuracy figure was about 1 part in 1000.

A large machine[9] with electrical interconnections was installed after the war at the National Physical Laboratory, England. This machine comprised 20 integrators with other associated units. Separate servo-systems each incorporating their own electronic amplifiers drove the input shafts of all units. Interconnection between the driving and driven shafts was achieved by a manual telephone type central connection board. The accuracy of individual units of the machine was about 1 part in 10,000.

Despite this high degree of precision obtained with the mechanical analyser, the relatively slow speed of operation proved to be a serious disadvantage for the investigation of problems in which numerous solutions were required for different parameter conditions. Again in many control systems involving computational techniques, the speed of mechanical units proved to be a serious drawback.

These drawbacks led to the development of the electromechanical and electronic differential analyser during World War II although some earlier work was done in the late 'thirties. G. A. Philbrick (U.S.A.) is credited as having made use of electronic computing amplifiers during this period. The development of general purpose electronic machines proceeded during the wartime period in this country and the U.S.A. A team at the Telecommunications Research Establishment, Malvern, England (now the Radar Research Establishment) developed electronic[10] and electromechanical[11] computing techniques. The work of this team was carried on after World War II at the R.A.E. (Royal Aircraft Establishment) England, where some of the first general purpose electronic machines were designed.[12] The Sperry Gyroscope Company were the first company in England to design a general purpose electronic analyser.

During this period similar work was being carried out in the U.S.A. and the first published paper was by Ragazzini, Randall and Russell.[13] In 1947 the Reeves Instrument Corporation[14] developed a computer which was the forerunner of the present-day R.E.A.C. The first commercially available electronic machine in England was developed by Short Brothers and Harland Limited in 1952.[15,16]

Although these early electronic analysers had relatively poor component accuracy figures of 1 per cent or more, their chief virtue was the high speed of operation possible, particularly in the repetitive machines. Present-day electronic machines have been developed to a high degree of accuracy and static component accuracy figures of about 0·01 per cent are available. However this is probably the limit of accuracy which may be achieved under practical operating conditions.

Another limitation of the electronic and electromechanical machines is that integration can only be performed with respect to the independent variable 'time' and this restricts the types of functions which may be generated with the basic computing units.

These facts have led to the development of the incremental or digital differential analyser in an effort to achieve greater accuracy and the versatility of the mechanical integrator without a significant reduction in computing speed compared with that of the electronic analogue machine.

The incremental technique has been applied successfully to specialized tasks such as navigation and axis resolution, but the general purpose machine has not been in favour because of the relatively high cost compared with the conventional analogue machine. However, with the introduction of high speed and cheaper transistors this machine may yet become a serious rival.

2.2 PRINCIPLE OF OPERATION

Consider a general nth-order differential equation which may be expressed in the form

$$\frac{d^n y}{dx^n} = f\left(x, y, \frac{dy}{dx}, ..., \frac{d^{n-1} y}{dx^{n-1}}\right) \qquad (2.1)$$

where x is the independent variable, y is the dependent variable and f represents a generalized function of (x, y) and its first $(n-1)$ derivatives.

If we assume that the nth order derivative is known, the dependent variable y and its $(n-1)$ derivatives may be obtained by successive integration of the nth order derivative.

Let us now define the generalized computer variable which represents an equation variable y as V_y. V_y may be a shaft rotation, a voltage, or other physical quantity dependent on the physical form of the differential analyser.

The relation between the computer variable and the corresponding equation variable may be expressed as

$$V_{y,0} = a_{y,0}\, y \tag{2.2}$$

where $a_{y,0}$ is a constant called the amplitude scale factor and has dimensions of the form

$$\left(\frac{\text{Physical Units of Computer Variable}}{\text{Physical Units of Equation Variable}}\right)$$

Note: The notation used in this text is that the computer variable representing the ith derivative of a variable y_1 is denoted by $V_{y_1,i}$. The notation for a variable y (zero derivative) is therefore $V_{y,0}$. However, if there is no possibility of ambiguity the subscript '0' may be omitted. Thus if $V_{y,0}$ represents an angular displacement in radians and y represents a displacement in metres, $a_{y,0}$ has the dimensions $\left(\dfrac{\text{radians}}{\text{metres}}\right)$.

Similarly if
$$V_{y,1} = a_{y,1}\frac{dy}{dx} \tag{2.3}$$

then $a_{y,1}$ has dimensions $\dfrac{\text{radians}}{\text{metres/time}}$ if x represents time. If the independent variable x occurs explicitly in the equation, it is treated in the same way as the dependent variable.

Thus
$$V_{x,0} = a_{x,0}\, x \tag{2.4}$$

Thus if x again represents time, the dimensions of $a_{x,0}$ are $\dfrac{\text{radians}}{\text{time}}$.

Note: The generalized computer variable V, for a particular form of differential analyser, has a particular physical form to represent all equation variables, e.g. in an electronic machine, V is a voltage.

Consider now the independent variable x. We may wish to alter the rate of change of y and its derivatives with respect to x to suit the characteristics of the analyser or for some other reason.

For this type of scaling, we effect the linear transformation

$$\lambda = a_\lambda x$$

i.e.
$$d\lambda = a_\lambda\, dx$$

therefore
$$\frac{dy}{d\lambda} = \frac{1}{a_\lambda}\frac{dy}{dx} \tag{2.5}$$

and
$$\frac{d^n y}{d\lambda^n} = \frac{1}{a_\lambda^n}\frac{d^n y}{dx^n}$$

where a_λ is a constant and is called the *independent variable scale factor*.

For a particular equation, x may represent distance (metres) whilst λ may represent time (seconds). a_λ in this case has dimensions $\dfrac{\text{seconds}}{\text{metres}}$.

Note: The scale factor a_λ fulfils a different purpose from that of $a_{x\,0}$ [see equation (2.4)] and its choice is in no way determined by the latter.

Consider now the instrumentation of equation (2.1).

Let us denote computer variables as follows:

$$V_{y,0} = a_{y,0}\,y$$

$$V_{y,1} = a_{y,1}\frac{dy}{dx} = a_{y,1}\,a_\lambda\frac{dy}{d\lambda}$$

$$V_{y,n} = a_{y,n}\frac{d^n y}{dx^n} = a_{y,n}\,a_\lambda^n\frac{d^n y}{d\lambda^n}$$

$$V_{x,0} = a_{x,0}\,x$$

(2.6)

Substituting the values in equation (2.1) we get

$$\frac{V_{y,n}}{a_{y,n}} = f\!\left(\frac{V_{x,0}}{a_{x,0}}, \frac{V_{y,0}}{a_{y,0}}, \frac{V_{y,1}}{a_{y,1}}, ..., \frac{V_{y,n-1}}{a_{y,n-1}}\right)$$

$$V_{y,n} = g(V_{x,0}, V_{y,0}, V_{y,1}, ..., V_{y,n-1})$$

(2.7)

where the function g takes ino account the scale factors.

Fig. 2.1 is a simple line diagram and implies that all computing variables are measured with respect to a common reference line.

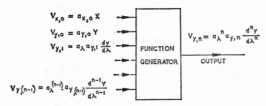

Fig. 2.1 *First step—the need for function generation*

The output of the function generator will be V_{yn} if we apply to its input terminals the variables $V_{x,0}, V_{y,0}, V_{y,1}, ..., V_{y,n-1}$, as dictated by equation (2.7). We now specify an integrating device called an integrator whose output V_0 is given by the expression

$$V_0 = K\int_{0+}^{\lambda_1} V_i\,d\lambda$$

(2.8)

where V_i is the input computer variable and K is a selected constant called the integrator coefficient. λ_1 is the period of integration.

Note: The integration between the limits $0 \vdash$ to λ_1 implies the insertion of the appropriate initial condition, i.e. the value of V_0 at $\lambda = 0+$. This value is inserted before the start of the computation period.

We also assume that there is no interaction between the output of one such integrator and the input of a following integrator or other computing units to which it is connected.

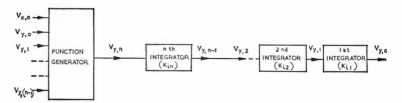

Fig. 2.2   *Second step—the need for integrato s*

$$V_{y,r} = a_{y,r}\, a_\lambda{}^r \frac{d^r y}{d\lambda^r} \quad for \ r = 0, 1 \dots n$$

$$K_{ir} = \frac{a_{y,r-1}}{a_\lambda a_{y,r}} \quad for \ r = 1, 2 \dots n$$

where K_{ir} is coefficient of the 'r-th' integrator

If therefore we connect n such integrators in series, we obtain representations of the first $(n-1)$ derivatives of y and the variable y as shown in Fig. 2.2.

For the rth integrator we have for the general case

$$V_{y,r-1} = K_{ir} \int_{0+}^{\lambda_1} V_{y,r}\, d\lambda$$

$$a_\lambda{}^{r-1} a_{y,r-1} \frac{d^{r-1} y}{d\lambda^{r-1}} = K_{ir}\, a_\lambda{}^r a_{y,r} \int \frac{d^r y}{d\lambda^r} d\lambda$$

$$= K_{ir}\, a_\lambda{}^r a_{y,r} \frac{d^{r-1} y}{d\lambda^{r-1}}$$

i.e. $$K_{ir} = \frac{a_{y,r-1}}{a_\lambda a_{y,r}} \tag{2.9}$$

where K_{ir} is the coefficient of the rth integrator. It is obvious, therefore, that if we choose K_{ir} to be a convenient value we have automatically chosen $a_{y,r}$ if $a_{y,r-1}$ and a_λ have been chosen. Thus we see that the independent variable scale factor a_λ is taken into account in the respective integrators and does not appear explicitly in the computing equations [see equation (2.7)]. We now connect the computer variables, at the outputs of the respective integrators, to the appropriate input terminals of the function generator in order to satisfy the original assumption that those variables were available.

The computer variable $V_{x,0} = a_{x,0} x$ is also applied to the input of the function generator and represents the forcing function of the equation.

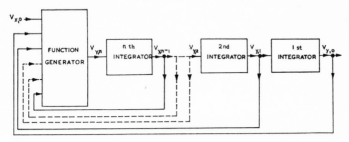

Fig. 2.3   *Third step—the final computing diagram*

This final arrangement is shown in Fig. 2.3. With this arrangement the computer variables $V_{y,0} \dots V_{y,n}$ represent the equation variables $y \dots \dfrac{d^n y_a}{dx^n}$ and plots of the variations of the computer variables with respect to λ constitute a graphical solution of the equation (2.1).

In the above instrumentation we have specified a generalized function generator which would, in general, be difficult to realize in physical terms as it would represent a function of n variables.

Fortunately, in many equations describing the performance of physical systems, the function generator required may be obtained by adding several simple mathematical functions.

To illustrate this point, let us consider some specific examples.

Example 2.1

Analysis of a series circuit comprising a discrete resistance R, inductance L and capacitance C (i.e. a series RLC circuit[16]) as shown in Fig. 2.4(a).

Case (a)

Consider the linear case in which R, L and C have constant time-invariant values.

The capacitor C has an initial charge q_0, at $t = 0$ when the switch S_1 is closed.

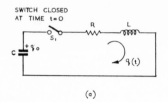

(a)

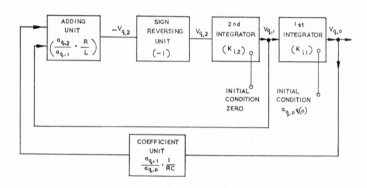

(b)

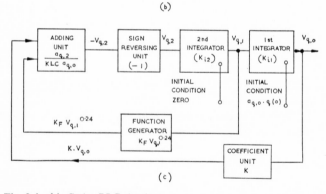

(c)

Fig. 2.4 (a) *Series RLC circuit*

(b) *Computing diagrams for circuit with linear time-invariant components*
Assumption $\dfrac{a_{q,1}}{a_{q,0}}\dfrac{1}{RC} \leqslant 1$ *otherwise coefficient unit would overload*

(c) *Computing diagrams for circuit in which the voltage across the*
resistor R is given by $e(t) = M\left(\dfrac{dq}{dt}\right)^{0.24}$ $K_F = KMCa_{q,0}\,a_{q,1}^{-0.24}$

(Note: the bracketed terms refer to the coefficients of the units)

24

The equation for charge $q(t)$ is

$$L\frac{d^2q}{dt^2} + R\frac{dq}{dt} + \frac{q}{c} = 0 \tag{2.10}$$

with initial conditions

$$\left.\begin{array}{l} q = q_0 \\[2mm] \dfrac{dq}{dt} = 0 \end{array}\right\} \text{at } t = 0 \tag{2.11}$$

Let the computer independent variable λ be expressed as

$$\lambda = a_\lambda t \tag{2.12}$$

To simplify matters, make $\qquad a_\lambda = 1$

so that $\qquad\qquad\qquad \lambda = t \tag{2.13}$

Denote the computer variables as

$$V_{q,0} = a_{q,0}q$$

$$V_{q,1} = a_{q,1}\frac{dq}{d\lambda} \tag{2.14}$$

$$V_{q,2} = a_{q,2}\frac{d^2q}{d\lambda^2}$$

with initial conditions

$$\left.\begin{array}{l} V_{q,0} = a_{q,0}q_0 \\[2mm] V_{q,1} = 0 \end{array}\right\} \text{at } \lambda = 0 \tag{2.15}$$

As before we express the highest derivative term as a function of the remaining terms

i.e. $$\frac{d^2q}{d\lambda^2} = -\frac{1}{L}\left(R\frac{dq}{d\lambda} + \frac{q}{C}\right) \tag{2.16}$$

The computer equation is therefore

$$V_{q,2} = -\frac{a_{q,2}}{L}\left(\frac{R}{a_{q,1}}V_{q,1} + \frac{1}{a_{q,0}C}V_{q,0}\right)$$

i.e. $$V_{q,2} = -\frac{a_{q,2}}{a_{q,1}}\frac{R}{L}\left(V_{q,1} + \frac{a_{q,1}}{a_{q,0}}\frac{1}{RC}V_{q,0}\right) \tag{2.17}$$

with the provision that the factor $\dfrac{a_{q,1}}{a_{q,0}}\dfrac{1}{RC} \leqq 1$

This equation may be written in the general form

$$V_{q,2} = g[V_{q,1}, V_{q,0}]$$

or
$$\frac{d^2q}{dt^2} = f\left[\frac{dq}{dt}, q\right] \qquad (2.18)$$

We note that in this example the generalized function g may be instrumented by the summation of the dependent variable and its first derivative with coefficients as dictated by equation (2.17). A possible computing arrangement based on equation (2.17) is shown in Fig. 2.4(b).

In this diagram we have specified three types of computing units in addition to the integrators. We make the assumption that there is no interaction between computing units:

(i) An adding unit whose essential property is that the output variable is equal to K times the sum of the input variables, where K is a selected coefficient.

(In our example $K = \dfrac{a_{q,2}}{a_{q,1}} \dfrac{R}{L}$.)

(ii) A *sign reversing* unit whose output variable is minus the input variable.

(iii) A coefficient unit whose output variable is A times the input variable, where A is a selected coefficient such that $A \leq 1$. This restriction on A is necessary since in our example, if $V_{q,0}$ is near its maximum value, A should not exceed unity if the output of the coefficient unit is not to exceed its maximum value.

(In our example $A = \dfrac{a_{q,1}}{a_{q,0}} \dfrac{1}{RC}$.)

With the arrangement shown in Fig. 2.4(b) the variations of computer variable $V_{q,0}$ and its derivatives with respect to the independent variable λ constitute a graphical solution of the time variation of q and its derivatives. *Note:* The first integrator has a finite initial condition $a_{q,0}q_0$, inserted before the start of the computation, which is actuated by the control circuits of the machine—we will enlarge on this aspect later.

Case (b)

L and C constant values.

R is a non-linear element whose voltage/current relationship is given by

$$e(t) = M[i(t)]^{0\cdot24} = M\left[\frac{dq}{dt}\right]^{0\cdot24} \qquad (2.19)$$

where $e(t)$ is the voltage applied to the element

$i(t)$ is the current flowing in the element

and M is a constant.

The equation for $q(t)$ under these conditions is

$$L\frac{d^2q}{dt^2} + M\left(\frac{dq}{dt}\right)^{0.24} + \frac{q}{C} = 0 \tag{2.20}$$

with initial conditions as before

$$\left.\begin{array}{l} q = q_0 \\[2mm] \dfrac{dq}{dt} = 0 \end{array}\right\} \text{at } t = 0 \tag{2.21}$$

Using the same scale factors as before we have for the computing equation:

$$V_{q,2} = -\frac{a_{q,2}}{L}\left[M\left(\frac{V_{q,1}}{a_{q,1}}\right)^{0.24} + \frac{1}{C}\frac{V_{q,0}}{a_{q,0}}\right]$$

$$= -\frac{a_{q,2}}{KLCa_{qo}}(KMCa_{q,0}\,a_{q,1}^{-0.24}\,V_{q,1}^{0.24} + KV_{q,0}) \tag{2.22}$$

where K is a scaling factor for the function generation

$$KMCa_{q,0}\,a_{q,1}^{-0.24}\,V_{q,1}^{0.24}$$

so that the value of this function does not exceed V_{max}.

Initial conditions are as before

i.e. $$\left.\begin{array}{l} V_{q,0}(0) = a_{q,0}q_0 \\[2mm] V_{q,0}(0) = 0 \end{array}\right\} \text{at } \lambda = 0 \tag{2.23}$$

A possible computing arrangement is shown in Fig. 2.4(c). It will be noted that we now require a function generator to produce the required function of the computer variable $V_{q,1}$, i.e. the output of this device is $Ma_{q,1}^{-0.24}(V_{q,1})^{0.24}KCa_{q,0}$. The generation of functions of one variable may be instrumented with comparative ease.

Example 2.2

Linear differential equation with time-varying coefficients[17]

e.g. $$\frac{d^2y}{dt^2} + [\omega_0^2 + \beta f(t)]y = 0 \tag{2.24}$$

where $f(t)$ is periodic with a mean value of zero and ω_0 and β are constants.

This is known as Hill's equation and it can be shown that all second order linear differential equations with periodic coefficients having a common fundamental frequency can be reduced to Hill's equation. The special case, which we will consider as a specific example, is given when $f(t) = \cos \omega_n t$, and is known as the Mathieu equation. (ω_n is a constant.)

i.e.
$$\frac{d^2 y}{dt^2} + (\omega_0^2 + \beta \cos \omega_n t) y = 0 \qquad (2.25)$$

with initial conditions

$$\left. \begin{aligned} y &= y_0 \\ \frac{dy}{dt} &= 0 \end{aligned} \right\} \text{at } t = 0 \qquad (2.26)$$

We may rewrite (2.25) as

$$\frac{d^2 y}{dt^2} + \omega_0^2 (1 + \alpha \cos \omega_n t) y = 0$$

where
$$\alpha = \frac{\beta}{\omega_0^2}$$

i.e.
$$\frac{d^2 y}{dt^2} = -\omega_0^2 (1 + \alpha \cos \omega_n t) y \qquad (2.27)$$

If we assign the computer variables as follows:

$$\lambda = t$$

$$V_{y,0} = a_{y,0} \, y$$

$$V_{y,1} = a_{y,1} \frac{dy}{d\lambda} \qquad (2.28)$$

$$V_{y,2} = a_{y,2} \frac{d^2 y}{d\lambda^2}$$

we arrive at the computer equation

$$V_{y,2} = -\frac{a_{y,2} \, \omega_0^2}{a_{y,0}} (1 + \alpha \cos \omega_n \lambda) V_{y,0} \qquad (2.29)$$

with initial conditions

$$\left. \begin{aligned} V_{y,0}(0) &= a_{y,0} \, y_0 \\ V_{y,1} \quad &= 0 \end{aligned} \right\} \text{at } \lambda = 0 \qquad (2.30)$$

28

The time-varying coefficient may be obtained by solving the equation

$$\frac{d^2 z}{d\lambda^2} + \omega_n^2 z = 0 \tag{2.31}$$

with initial conditions

$$\left.\begin{array}{r} z = \alpha k \\[2mm] \frac{dz}{d\lambda} = 0 \end{array}\right\} \text{ at } \lambda = 0 \tag{2.32}$$

Note: k is a scaling constant to suit circuit conditions.
The solution of this equation is

$$z = k\alpha \cos \omega_n \lambda \tag{2.33}$$

The computer equation corresponding to equation (2.31) is

$$V_{z,2} = -\omega_n^2 \frac{a_{z,2}}{a_{z,0}} V_{z,0} \tag{2.34}$$

with initial conditions

$$\left.\begin{array}{r} V_{z,0}(0) = k a_{z,0} \alpha \\[2mm] V_{z,1} = 0 \end{array}\right\} \text{at } \lambda = 0 \tag{2.35}$$

Substituting $\alpha \cos \omega_n \lambda = \dfrac{V_{z,0}}{a_{z,0} \cdot k}$ in equation (2.29) and denoting a multiply-

ing constant K_M, we have

$$V_{y,2} = -\frac{a_{y,2} \omega_0^2}{a_{y,0}} \left[V_{y,0} + K_M (V_{y,0} V_{z,0}) \left(\frac{1}{k K_M a_{z,0}} \right) \right] \tag{2.36}$$

The computer diagram for the solution of equation (2.36) is shown in Fig. 2.5.

In this diagram we have introduced another computing unit called a *multiplier* whose output variable is K_M times the product of the two input variables. (K_M is the constant multiplier coefficient.)

Example 2.3

Simultaneous linear differential equations with constant coefficients

$$\left.\begin{array}{r} 3\dfrac{dx}{dt} + 2x + \dfrac{dy}{dt} = 1 \\[4mm] \dfrac{dx}{dt} + 3y + \dfrac{4dy}{dt} = 0 \end{array}\right\} \tag{2.37}$$

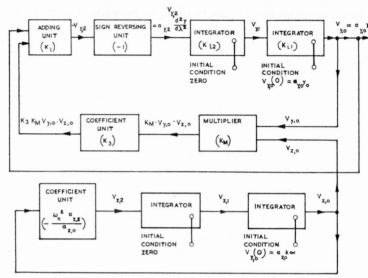

Fig. 2.5 *Solution of Mathieu equation*

Coefficients $K_{i2} = \dfrac{a_{y,1}}{a_{y,2}}$ $K_{i1} = \dfrac{a_{y,0}}{a_{y,1}}$ $K_1 = \dfrac{a_{y,2}\omega_0{}^2}{a_{y,0}}$ $K_3 = \dfrac{1}{kK_M a_{z,0}}$

with initial conditions $\left.\begin{array}{l} x = 0 \\ y = 0 \end{array}\right\}$ at $t = 0$ $\qquad$ (2.38)

Rearranging terms we have

$$\frac{dx}{dt} = -\frac{1}{3}\left(2x + \frac{dy}{dt} - 1\right)$$

$$\frac{dy}{dt} = -\frac{1}{4}\left(3y + \frac{dx}{dt}\right) \qquad (2.39)$$

In this example let us choose an independent variable scale factor other than unity,

i.e. $$\lambda = a_\lambda t$$

$$\frac{dx}{d\lambda} = \frac{dx}{a_\lambda dt}$$

and $$\frac{d^n x}{d\lambda^n} = \frac{d^n x}{a_\lambda^n dt^n} \qquad (2.40)$$

Similarly $$\frac{d^n y}{d\lambda^n} = \frac{d^n y}{a_\lambda^n dt^n}$$

Substituting these values in equation (2.39) we have

$$\frac{dx}{d\lambda} = -\frac{1}{3a_\lambda}\left[2x + a_\lambda\frac{dy}{d\lambda} - 1\right]$$

$$\frac{dy}{d\lambda} = -\frac{1}{4a_\lambda}\left[3y + a_\lambda\frac{dx}{d\lambda}\right] \tag{2.41}$$

Consider now the amplitude scale factors,

$$V_{x,0} = a_{x,0}\, x$$

$$V_{x,1} = a_{x,1}\frac{dx}{dt} = a_{x,1}\, a_\lambda\frac{dx}{d\lambda}$$

$$V_{y,0} = a_{y,0}\, y \tag{2.42}$$

$$V_{y,1} = a_{y,1}\frac{dy}{dt} = a_{y,1}\, a_\lambda\frac{dy}{d\lambda}$$

Substituting these values in equation (2.41), we have

$$V_{x,1} = -\frac{a_{x,1}}{3}\left[2\frac{V_{x,0}}{a_{x,0}} + \frac{V_{y,1}}{a_{y,1}} - 1\right]$$

$$V_{y,1} = -\frac{a_{y,1}}{4}\left[3\frac{V_{y,0}}{a_{y,0}} + \frac{V_{x,1}}{a_{x,1}}\right] \tag{2.43}$$

Assume now that we wish to make $a_\lambda = 10$, i.e. we wish to slow down the variation of V with respect to λ by a factor of 10 compared with the variations of x and y with respect to t.

Note: The choice of the independent variable scale factor and the amplitude scale factors is based on a knowledge of the physical system under consideration and the limitations of the differential analyser being used.

Let us now assume that we know that the approximate maximum value of x is 0·5 units and that of y, 0·2 units. In addition estimated maximum values of dx/dt and dy/dt are 0·2 and 0·1 respectively.

Assume also that the maximum amplitude range of the computing units is ± 100 units of V.

Now $V_{x,0} = a_{x,0}\, x$

with $x_{max} \simeq 0.5$

Since $V_{x,0}(max) \leq 100$

make $a_{x,0} = 100$ (units of V per unit of x)

Also
$$V_{x,1} = a_{x,1}\frac{dx}{dt}$$

$$\frac{dx}{dt}(\max) \simeq 0\cdot2$$

Therefore make
$$a_{x,1} = 250$$

$$V_{y,0}(\max) = a_{y,0}\,y_{\max}$$

$$\simeq 0\cdot2 a_{y,0}$$

Therefore make
$$a_{y,0} = 250$$

$$V_{y,1}(\max) = a_{y,1}\frac{dy}{dt}(\max)$$

$$\simeq a_{y,1}(0\cdot1)$$

Therefore make
$$a_{y,1} = 500$$

Note: The maximum values of the computer variables will be approximately half that of the possible maximum, thus ensuring a good signal to noise ratio, and adequate allowance for possible errors in the estimates of amplitudes of the problem variables.

If we now incorporate these amplitude scale factors and independent variable scale factor in equation (2.43), we have

$$V_{x,1} = -\frac{250}{3}\left(2\,\frac{V_{x,0}}{100}+\frac{V_{y,1}}{500}-1\right)$$

i.e.
$$V_{x,1} = -\tfrac{5}{3}(V_{x,0}+0\cdot1V_{y,1}-50) \tag{2.44}$$

$$V_{y,1} = -\frac{500}{4}\left(3\,\frac{V_{y,0}}{250}+\frac{V_{x,1}}{250}\right)$$

i.e.
$$V_{y,1} = -\tfrac{3}{2}(V_{y,0}+\tfrac{1}{3}V_{x,1}) \tag{2.45}$$

The simulation of equations (2.44) and (2.45) is shown in block diagram form in Fig. 2.6. With $a_\lambda = 10$, $K_{ix} = 1/25$ and $K_{iy} = 1/20$.

Note: In Fig. 2.6, a_λ is assumed to be unity, giving $K_{ix} = 1/2\cdot5$ and $K_{iy} = 1/2$. The initial condition on each integrator is zero.

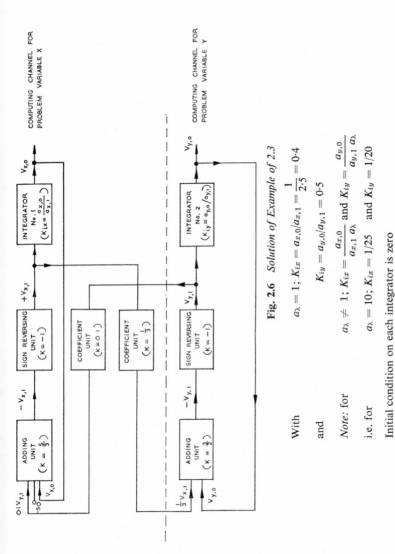

Fig. 2.6 *Solution of Example of 2.3*

With $\qquad a_\lambda = 1; K_{ix} = a_{x,0}/a_{x,1} = \dfrac{1}{2\cdot 5} = 0\cdot 4$

and $\qquad K_{iy} = a_{y,0}/a_{y,1} = 0\cdot 5$

Note: for $\quad a_\lambda \neq 1; K_{ix} = \dfrac{a_{x,0}}{a_{x,1}\,a_\lambda} \quad$ and $\quad K_{iy} = \dfrac{a_{y,0}}{a_{y,1}\,a_\lambda}$

i.e. for $\quad a_\lambda = 10; K_{ix} = 1/25 \quad$ and $K_{iy} = 1/20$

Initial condition on each integrator is zero

33

2.3 BASIC REQUIREMENTS

Computing Units

We may summarize the basic computing units required by considering the last few examples.

(i) *Linear Differential Equations with Constant Coefficients*

A computing channel is required for each problem variable. The number of integrators in each channel is equal to the order of the equation in the variable being represented. One adding unit is required in each computing channel. (As will be discussed later it is, however, possible to combine the functions of addition and integration in the integrator unit.) In addition coefficient units and sign reversing units are required to enable the coefficient of the problem variables to be set up on the analyser.

All computing units are assumed to have zero output impedance, i.e. units connected in cascade do not load one another.

The properties of the four basic units: integrator, adding unit, coefficient unit and sign reversing unit are as follows:

$$
\left.
\begin{aligned}
\textit{Integrator} \qquad & V_{o_i} = K_i \int_{0+}^{\lambda} V_i \, d\lambda \\[2ex]
\textit{Adding Unit} \qquad & V_{o_a} = K_a \sum_{1}^{n} V_i \\[2ex]
\textit{Coefficient Unit} \qquad & V_{o_c} = K_c V_i \\[2ex]
\textit{Sign Reversing Unit} \qquad & V_o = -V_i
\end{aligned}
\right\} \qquad (2.46)
$$

where V_i is input computer variable (or variables), V_0 is the output computer variable, K is the constant coefficient of the unit (which may be selected).

Note: K_i has dimensions λ^{-1}.

(ii) *Linear Differential Equations with Coefficients comprising Variation of the Independent Variable*

Example 2.2. illustrates a typical case when time is the independent variable.

For this type of problem, we need a function generator of the independent variable, in addition to the units described in (i).

As in example 2.2, the required function may be obtained by solving a subsidiary linear differential equation, but in the more general use a special function generator must be provided.

In addition to this generator we require a multiplier or multipliers to produce the required coefficients.

The properties of these two units are as follows:

Function Generator

$$V_o = f(\lambda) \tag{2.47}$$

where $f(\lambda)$ denotes a function of independent computer variable λ.

Multiplier

$$V_o = K_M V_x V_y \tag{2.48}$$

where V_x and V_y are input computer variables and K_M is the multiplier constant coefficient.

(iii) *Non-Linear Differential Equations*

In addition to the computing units already discussed we require a more general form of function generator whose output computer variable V_o is given by

$$V_o = f(V_1, V_2, ..., V_n, \lambda) \tag{2.49}$$

where $V_1, V_2, ..., V_n$ are input computer variables.

As already stated a generator of this form is extremely difficult to realize and the most common form is a function generator of one variable,

i.e. $$V_o = f(V_i)$$

Other specialized forms of function generators will be discussed in a later chapter.

2.4 BASIC ANCILLARY REQUIREMENTS

The facilities provided obviously depend on the type and complexity of machine, but the basic requirement may be specified as follows:

(i) A source of power to supply the various units with the necessary arrangements to ensure the correct sequence of application. Arrangements are usually made (manual or automatic) so that the power is switched on, for a running-up period before the start of a computation, to minimize the effect of temperature variations.

(ii) A means for inserting initial conditions in integrators. The latter are said to be in the 'set' position when the initial conditions are being set.

(iii) A flexible and tidy method of interconnecting the units as dictated by the problem under consideration. In the mechanical machine this is effected by coupling shafts and gears, and in the electronic machine by means of electrical cables or 'patch cords'.

(iv) A method of starting and stopping the computation period at controlled instants of time. At the start of the computation, this implies the simultaneous change-over of all integrators from the 'set' position to the 'compute' position. The latter position allows each integrator to start computing from the required initial value.

In some machines (at the end of computation) the values of all integrator outputs are maintained by removing the input variables. The integrators in this condition are said to be in the 'hold' position. A further facility which is sometimes provided is the provision for changing one or more integrators from 'set condition' to 'hold condition' during the computation.

(v) A means for setting coefficients of all units. This may be arranged for manual or automatic setting.

(vi) A method for measuring and/or recording the solutions. For the slower type machine the recorder is usually of the form of a plotting table or pen-recorder whilst in the faster electronic machine (particularly the repetitive operation machine) a cathode ray oscillograph may also be used. Facilities are usually provided for checking the current operation of all units. The mechanical machine, due to lack of space, will not be described in this text. The reader is referred to References 7, 8 and 9 for good descriptions of the machine and its capabilities. It may be noted again that the mechanical integrator is more versatile than its electronic counterpart in that it can integrate with respect to a variable other than time. For this reason there may be certain applications, even today, where the mechanical integrator may be used to advantage.

However, for high speed calculations, hybrid (i.e. analogue/digital) computation methods, or iterative methods of operation of the electronic machine are employed to give the facility of performing integration with respect to several variables.

2.5 THE ELECTRONIC MACHINE

2.5.1 Basic Operations

In this machine all problem variables are represented by voltages measured with respect to a common reference line (usually at earth potential).

The basic element is a high gain, directly coupled amplifier with a sign reversal between input and output signals at zero frequency. This element is usually called an 'operational amplifier' or 'computing amplifier' and is represented schematically in Fig. 2.7.

The relationship between output voltage $e_o(t)$ and input voltage $e_i(t)$ is given by

$$e_o(t) = -Ke_i(t) \tag{2.50}$$

where K is a positive constant representing the forward voltage gain of the amplifier.

Note: A voltage which is a function of time t is written as $e(t)$.

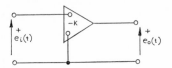

Fig. 2.7 *Operational amplifier*

$$e_0(t) = -Ke_i(t)$$

This is an approximate relationship since in an actual amplifier the forward gain will be a function of frequency and the amplifier will introduce its own phase shift. It is the task of the computer designer, however, to ensure that the above approximation is valid for all practical network configurations with which the amplifier is associated. As this point will be discussed more fully later it will suit our purposes at the moment to consider the above approximation to be valid.

Other properties of the operational amplifier, which we may assume to be valid at the moment, are as follows:

(i) the input impedance is infinite, i.e. no current flows out of or into the input terminal.
(ii) the output impedance is zero.

The basic mathematical operations of integration with respect to time, addition, multiplication by a constant, sign reversal, are achieved by such an amplifier associated with passive elements in the form of resistors and capacitors.

Integration with Respect to Time

Consider the network illustrated in Fig. 2.8 where there are n input resistors $R_1, R_2, ..., R_n$ to which are applied voltages $e_1(t) ... e_n(t)$ respectively measured with respect to the common line. A feedback capacitor having a capacitance C is connected between the output and input terminals of the amplifier.

$e_o(t)$ is again the output voltage.

Point 'a' is called the 'summing point' for obvious reasons and the voltage at this point is denoted by e_s.

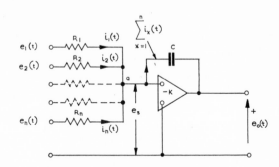

Fig. 2.8 *Summation and integration*

$$e_0(t) = -\left[\frac{1}{R_1 C}\int e_1(t)\,dt + \frac{1}{R_2 C}\int e_2(t)\,dt + \dots \frac{1}{R_n C}\int e_n(t)\,dt\right]$$

Apply Ohm's Law

$$i_1(t) = \frac{e_1(t) - e_s(t)}{R_1} \qquad i_2(t) = \frac{e_2(t) - e_s()}{R_2} \qquad i_n(t) = \frac{e_n(t) - e_s(t)}{R_n} \qquad (2.51)$$

where $i(t)$ represents current as a function of time.

Applying Kirchhoff's Nodal Law

$$\sum_{x=1}^{n} i_x(t) = i_1(t) + i_2(t) + \dots + i_n(t) \qquad (2.52)$$

Now $\sum_{x=1}^{n} i_x(t)$ is the current flowing through the capacitor C since there is no current flow to the input of the amplifier.

Therefore

$$\sum_{x=1}^{n} i_x(t) = i_1(t) + i_2(t) + \dots + i_n(t) = C\frac{d}{dt}[e_s(t) - e_o(t)] \qquad (2.53)$$

From equation (2.50) we have

$$e_o(t) = -Ke_s(t)$$

38

If we now assume that $K \to \infty$ so that $e_s(t) = [-e_o(t)/K] \to 0$ we may ignore $e_s(t)$ compared with the other voltages present. With this assumption the approximate relationships are as follows:

$$i_1(t) + i_2(t) + \ldots i_n(t) = \frac{e_1(t)}{R_1} + \frac{e_2(t)}{R_2} + \frac{e_n(t)}{R_n} = -C\frac{d}{dt}e_o(t)$$

i.e. $\quad e_o(t) = -\left[\frac{1}{R_1 C}\int e_1(t)\,dt + \frac{1}{R_2 C}\int e_2(t)\,d + \frac{1}{R_n C}\int e_n(t)\,dt\right]$ \quad (2.54)

Thus summation and integration with respect to the independent variable time has been achieved.

For the particular case of integration of one variable we have the situation illustrated in Fig. 2.9.

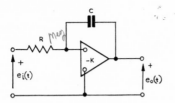

Fig. 2.9 *Integrator unit*

$$e_0(t) = -\frac{1}{RC}\int e_i(t)\,dt$$

This is a special case of Fig. 2.8

and $\qquad\qquad e_o(t) = -\frac{1}{RC}\int e_i(t)\,dt$ \qquad\qquad (2.55)

The product RC in any consistent system of units has the dimensions of time. If R is expressed in megohms (10^6 ohms) and C is expressed in microfarads (10^{-6} farad), the units of the product are

$$\text{ohms} \times 10^6 \times \text{farads} \times 10^{-6} \quad \text{i.e. ohms} \times \text{farads}$$

which has the dimensions of seconds.

The product RC is usually denoted by τ where τ is called the *integrator time constant*.

Note: It is a time constant.

Equation (2.55) may be written as

$$e_o(t) = -\frac{1}{\tau}\int e_i(t)\,d$$ \qquad\qquad (2.56)

Compare with equation (2.46) where, for the mechanical integrator, the dimension of $1/K_i$ is not necessarily time.

Addition or Summation

Consider Fig. 2.10.

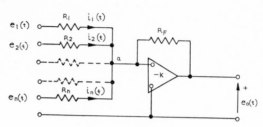

Fig. 2.10   *Adding unit*

$$e_0(t) = -\left[\frac{R_F}{R_1} e_1(t) + \frac{R_F}{R_2} e_2(t) + \dots \frac{R_F}{R_n} e_n(t)\right]$$

In this case the capacitor C in Fig. 2.8 is replaced by a resistor R_F. Under the same assumptions as before

$$\sum_{x=1}^{n} i_x(t) = \frac{e_1(t)}{R_1} + \frac{e_2(t)}{R_2} + \dots \frac{e_n(t)}{R_n} = -\frac{e_o(t)}{R_F}$$

therefore

$$e_o(t) = -\left[\frac{R_F}{R_1} e_1(t) + \frac{R_F}{R_2} e_2(t) \dots \frac{R_F}{R_n} e_n(t)\right]$$

i.e.

$$e_o(t) = -[a_1 e_1(t) + a_2 e_2(t) + \dots a_n e_n(t)] \tag{2.57}$$

where $a_1 \dots a_n$ are selected constant coefficients given by

$$a_1 = \frac{R_F}{R_1} \dots a_n = \frac{R_F}{R_n}$$

Thus addition of n input voltages has been achieved.

Multiplication by a Constant

This is a special case of the above with only one input resistor

so that

$$e_o(t) = -\frac{R_F}{R_1} e_i(t)$$

$$= -ae_i(t) \tag{2.58}$$

where

$$a = \frac{R_F}{R_1}$$

Sign Reversal

This is a special case of the above with $a = 1$,

i.e. $$R_F = R_1$$

so that $$e_o(t) = -e_i(t) \tag{2.59}$$

Note: There is a negative sign in all the above relationships due to the presence of the operational amplifier.

Multiplication by a Constant less than Unity

Multiplication by a constant less than unity is obtained by means of a discrete potential divider arrangement or by a continuous precision potentiometer with a calibrated dial. These potentiometers are usually

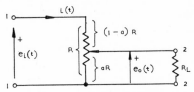

Fig. 2.11 *Potentiometer unit*

$$e_0(t) = ae_i(t) \quad if \ R_L \to \infty$$

adjusted to three significant figures either manually or automatically (by means of a servo-mechanism). The basic potentiometer circuit is shown in Fig. 2.11 where R_L represents the load resistance (which is usually the input resistance to an amplifier).

If a calibrated dial, based on a linear relationship between rotation of the potentiometer spindle and the resistance between the wiper and terminal as represented by aR is used, the value of R_L must be such that negligible current flows through it compared with the current $i(t)$ in Fig. 2.11.

Assuming for the moment that the effect of R_L may be neglected

we have $$i(t) = \frac{e_i(t)}{R}$$

$$e_o(t) = i(t)aR = ae_i(t) \tag{2.60}$$

The output resistance R_o of the potentiometer, i.e. the output resistance at terminals 2 2 with terminals 1 1 open circuited, is given by

$$R_o = \frac{aR(1-a)R}{R} = a(1-a)R \tag{2.61}$$

$$\frac{dR_o}{da} = R(1-2a)$$

For the maximum value of R_o

$$\frac{dR_o}{da} = 0$$

therefore $\qquad\qquad\qquad 1 - 2a = 0$

i.e. $\qquad\qquad\qquad\qquad a = \tfrac{1}{2}$

i.e. maximum output impedance occurs when the wiper is at the mid-position.

The maximum value of R_o is therefore given by

$$R_o(\text{max}) = 0\cdot5(1 - 0\cdot5)R = \frac{R}{4}$$

If now $R_L = 1000(R/4)$, the error in neglecting the effect of R_L will be approximately 1 part in 1000.

If the potentiometers are set by a servo arrangement the loading effect of R_L is taken into account since the wiper will be moved to a position such that $e_o(t) = ae_i$ (where a is the desired coefficient) with R_L connected. The basic arrangement of this method is shown in Fig. 2.12.

A servo-amplifier–servo-motor combination is fed with an input voltage E obtained from a precision potential divider system (discrete or continuous) supplied from the computer standard reference voltage (usually 100 V).

The servo motor is connected via clutches to a number of potentiometers. Each of the latter is adjusted in turn by

(i) energizing the appropriate clutch to connect the potentiometer shaft to the motor shaft.
(ii) Switching the potentiometer and terminal from its normal connection to the standard reference voltage.
(iii) Connecting the load resistor R_L to earth potentiometer.
(iv) Connecting the output voltage of the potentiometer wiper to the input of the servo amplifier for comparison with the input voltage.

With connections made we have a position control system. A voltage $E = ae$, where a is the desired coefficient, forms the input voltage, and the servo motor rotates the potentiometer shaft until the output voltage of the potentiometer cancels out this voltage within a specified error depending on the accuracy of the feedback control system.

When this action is complete the clutch is de-energized and the potentiometer and resistor R_L switched to their normal connections. The input reference potential divider is usually in a discrete decade form so that push

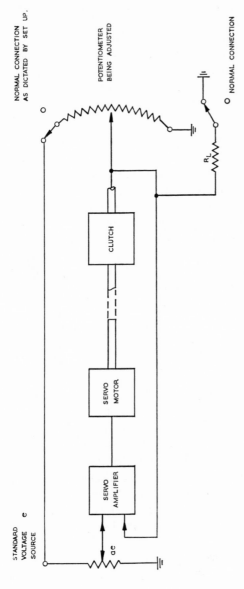

Fig. 2.12 *Servo setting of potentiometer*

buttons representing decimal digits may be operated to represent the decimal coefficient. A separate arrangement of switches, selected by push buttons, operate the desired potentiometer and associated load resistor.

A further refinement, which is now available in commercial machines is that the potentiometers are selected and set to the appropriate values by means of a tape reader which reads tape on which is punched, in a binary notation, the information regarding the particular potentiometer to be set and the value of the setting. The output pulses from the tape reader are used to actuate the necessary switches and clutches.

2.5.2 Interconnections

In some small machines, comprising say twenty operational amplifiers, connections between one unit and another are made directly by electrical cables using plug and socket arrangements. This method although simple and straightforward presents a rather untidy array of cables when the set-up is completed, and checking of interconnnections is very difficult.

To obviate this difficulty modern machines have a set-up or patch panel which may be removable. To this panel are connected all relevant terminals of the computing units, which are disposed in a logical geo-metrical array, so that interconnections may be made by two-pin shorting plugs or short lengths of cable.

If, however, the machine is not intended for general purpose applications, the interconnections may be wired permanently for the particular repre-sentation of the system under investigation.

A modern development is an automatic patching arrangement operated from punched paper tape with a manual over-ride usually incorporated.

An experimental version of an automatic patching system[19] has been developed at the College of Aeronautics, Cranfield. In this system connections between computing units are made by the use of uni-selectors. Although there are no commercial machines with automatic patching as yet available, it would seem probable that the incorporation of this facility will be necessary especially for a large machine integrated with a digital computer to control industrial plant. Again with automatic patching the analogue machine may be operated as an adaptive computer and as such may be incorporated in adaptive control systems.

2.5.3 Mode Control of Integrators

The integrator unit (with the exception of more general active networks described in Chapter 6) is the only one in which the relationship between output voltage and input voltage is a function of time. It is necessary, therefore, to have the correct time sequence of control so that the integrator may perform in the desired manner. The required conditions (modes) of the integrator may be classified as follows:

(i) 'Set' mode: In this condition the integrator control circuit is arranged so that the integrator capacitor may be changed to the desired initial condition voltage. This mode is sometimes called the 'initial condition' mode.

(ii) 'Compute' mode: In this condition the integrator has the capability of integrating the input voltages with respect to time, with the correct initial condition voltage at the start of the compute period, i.e. when $\lambda = 0$.

(iii) 'Hold' mode: This is the condition in which all inputs to the integrator are removed. If the integrator is perfect its output voltage will remain constant at the value when switching occurred, i.e. the integrator holds or stores the value of its output voltage at the instant at which switching occurs.

A typical integrator circuit is shown in Fig. 2.13 (a) in which the normal input variables $e_1(t) \dots e_n(t)$ are connected via resistors $R_1 \dots R_n$ through relay contacts A_1 to the grid input of the amplifier. An initial condition voltage e_{IC} at terminal I_2 is also connected via resistor R_i and contacts B_1 to the grid input of the amplifier.

The 'set' mode is given when contacts B_1 are closed and contacts A_1 are open, as illustrated in Fig. 2.13 (a).

Under these conditions a constant voltage e_{IC} will result in an output voltage $e_o(t)$ given by

$$e_o(t) = -e_{IC}\left[1 - \exp\left(-\frac{t}{R_i C}\right)\right]$$

The situation is illustrated in Fig. 2.13 (b). If the period of the 'set' mode, $t = T_1$, is such that $T_1/R_i C \gg 1$, the capacitor C will charge to the voltage $-e_{IC}$ within a small percentage error. For example, if $T_1/R_i C = 10$, the error is less than 0·005 per cent. At the termination of the 'set' period contacts B_1 are opened and A_1 closed to put the integrator into the 'compute' mode in which the integrator integrates the input variables over the period T_2 to give the solution, with the initial condition $e_o = -e_{IC}$. For repetitive operation, this sequence of operations is repeated automatically by energizing the relays A and B by the appropriate control signal in the correct time sequence. If all integrators are operated simultaneously, in this way, we have synchronous repetitive operation of the computer and the solution will be repeated at the repetition rate of the control sequence. If this repetition rate is several times a second, a steady image of the solution may be obtained on a cathode ray tube with a significant afterglow.

This facility is a significant advantage for applications in which the operator wishes to assess quickly the effect of parameter variations on the solution, in order to get a better appreciation of the problem under investigation. An accurate solution may be obtained later by increasing

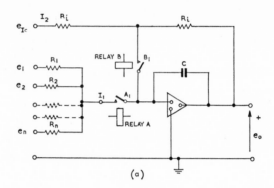

(a)

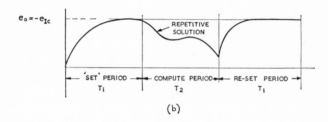

(b)

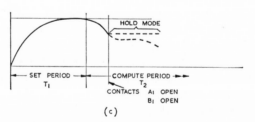

(c)

Fig. 2.13 *Mode control of integrator*

(a) *Typical integrator unit*   (b) *Output voltage during 'set' and 'compute' modes*
for repetitive operation   (c) *Output voltage during 'hold' mode*

the time scale factor to slow down the time sequence of events and record the solution, under manual control of the compute period, on an accurate pen-recorder or plotting table. If the mode control is switched from repetitive operation to manual operation the compute period is then under the control of the operator. This mode of operation is sometimes called 'single shot' operation.

The 'hold' condition is given when both contacts A_1 and B_1 are open as illustrated in Fig. 2.13 (c) and this condition may be actuated automatically when one or more computer variables reach a critical value or after a certain period. This facility is an obvious advantage in problems

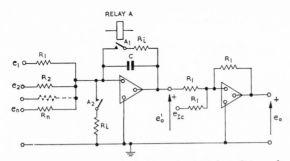

Fig. 2.14 *Alternative method of inserting initial condition voltage*

where such conditions are of interest. Alternatively the 'hold' condition may be applied in a repetitive manner to all integrators for a fixed period between the 'set' mode and the 'compute' period. This permits the facility of recording all computer variables after a compute run.

For high speed repetitive operation, an alternative arrangement of inserting the initial condition voltage is shown in Fig. 2.14. This method was used in the early Short machine,[16] with a repetition rate of 100 times a second, to give a short charge and discharge period of the integrator capacitor.

In this arrangement one integrator mode relay A is used with two contacts A_1 and A_2. For the 'set' mode A_1 and A_2 are closed to discharge capacitor C to zero potential. The initial voltage e_{IC} is applied to the input of the following sign reverser as shown. In the 'compute' mode contacts A_1 and A_2 are opened and the initial condition voltage is added to the output of the integrator, starting from a zero initial condition, to give the final output voltage e_o.

The disadvantage of this method is the need for the extra sign reverser for every integrator with an initial condition other than zero. Furthermore it is not possible to have a 'hold' mode.

A more modern circuit for high speed repetitive operation is shown in Fig. 2.15 where an extra change-over relay C has been incorporated. The purpose of this relay is to provide a low time constant $R_o C$ for charging and discharging the capacitor so that the resistor R_i may remain a reasonable value and thus obviate the need for a large current drain from the reference supply voltage. In this arrangement, the 'set' mode is given with contacts A_1 open, B_1 closed and contact C_1 made. 'Compute' mode is given with contact B_1 open, contact C_2 made and A_1 closed.

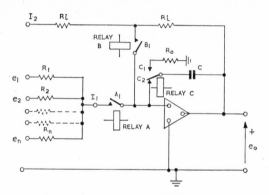

Fig. 2.15 *Integrator circuit for high speed switching*

'Hold' mode is given with contacts A_1 and B_1 open and contact C_2 made.

The integrator in the 'hold' mode will retain its output voltage, within a certain error, over a particular period. The deviation from the fixed value is due to (i) amplifier leakage current (ii) a resistance path across the capacitor and absorption effects in the capacitor dielectric. A typical drift figure for a good quality integrator is in the range 10–100 microvolts per second depending on the value of C. This effect is discussed in a later chapter.

For very high repetitive operation (exceeding 100 times a second) the electromechanical relays are replaced by transistor switches as described in Chapter 5.

We have restricted our attention, so far, to synchronous repetitive control of the integrators. A modern variation on this theme is asynchronous control in which several integrators may be in the 'hold' mode, others in the 'compute' mode and the remainder in the 'set' mode. This facility permits better utilization of the inherent storage, or memory, of the integrator and, as described in Chapter 5, results in the facility of iterative methods of solution.

REFERENCES

1. W. Thomson (Lord Kelvin): 'Mechanical Integration of the Linear Differential Equations of the Second Order with Variable Coefficients', *Proc. Roy. Soc.*, 1876, **23**, pp. 269–71.

2. W. Thomson: 'Mechanical Integration of the General Linear Differential Equations of any Order with Variable Coefficients', *Proc. Roy. Soc.*, 1876, **24**, pp. 271–5.

3. V. Bush: 'The Differential Analyzer—A New Machine for Solving Differential Equations', *J. Franklin Inst.*, 1931, **212**, pp. 447–88.

4. C. W. Nieman: *American Machinist*, 1927, **66**, p. 895.

5. D. R. Hartree: *Nature*, 1935, **135**, p. 940; *Nature*, 1940, **146**, p. 319.

6. D. R. Hartree: *Calculating Instruments and Machines* (Cambridge University Press, 1949).

7. J. Crank: *The Differential Analyzer* (Longmans, Green, 1947).

8. V. Bush and S. M. Caldwell: 'A New Type of Differential Analyzer', *J. Franklin Inst.*, 1945, **240**, p. 255.

9. J. G. L. Michel: 'The Mechanical Differential Analyzer—Recent Developments and Applications', *Proceedings of the International Analogy Computation Meeting, Brussels, September, 1955*, pp. 245–53.

10. F. C. Williams: 'Electronic Servo Simulators', *J. Inst. Elec. Engng.*, 1947, **94**, Part II A, pp. 112–29.

11. F. C. Williams and A. M. Uttley: 'The Velodyne', *J. Inst. Elec. Engng.*, 1946, **93**, Part III A, p. 317.

12. C. A. A. Wass: *An Introduction to Electronic Analogue Computers* (Pergamon Press, 1955).

13. J. R. Ragazzini, R. H. Randall and F. A. Russell: 'Analysis of Problems in Dynamics by Electronic Circuits', *Proc. I.R.E.*, 1947, pp. 444–52.

14. C. L. Johnson: *Analog Computer Techniques* (McGraw-Hill, 1956).

15. R. J. A. Paul: 'The Short Electronic Analogue Computer', *The Overseas Engineer*, 1956, XXIX, **337**, pp. 205–8.

16. R. J. A. Paul and E. Lloyd-Thomas: 'The Design and Applications of a General Purpose Analogue Computer', *J. Brit. I.R.E.*, 1957, **17**, pp. 49–73.

17. R. L. Cosgriff: *Non-Linear Control Systems* (McGraw-Hill, 1958).

18. I. I. Eterman: *Analogue Computers* (Translated from Russian by G. Segal) (Pergamon Press, 1960).

19. R. N. Rao: 'Logical Design of an Analogue Computer Patching System using Punched Tape Setting-up Data', College of Aeronautics Thesis, 1960.

Chapter 3

PROGRAMMING, SCALING AND CHECKING PROCEDURES

3.1 THE PREPARATION OF THE PROBLEM

IT IS NECESSARY TO OBTAIN A PRECISE STATEMENT OF THE PROBLEM before programming of the computer is contemplated. In many cases the problem may not be stated in analytical terms, such as a set of differential equations, but in a more descriptive manner. For such cases a mathematical model of the system under investigation must be derived. Several topological forms of the model may be attempted and it is necessary to assess which form lends itself most easily to simulation or, alternatively, those parts of the model which may be solved by analogue means and those parts which are best solved by digital means. At this stage it may be necessary to check that the chosen model represents a reasonable approximation to the system. This confirmation may be obtained by comparing the model and system performance with certain simplifying assumptions. A typical simplification is to assume linear operation over a restricted range of variables. With the satisfactory conclusion of these preliminary investigations we have a mathematical model comprising sets of mathematical relationships between variables. These relationships may be in the form of ordinary differential equations, algebraic equations or partial differential equations. The detailed programming steps involved depend on the type of equation to be solved and these are discussed in later chapters.

For our purposes at the moment, we will restrict our attention in this chapter to the computer programme for solutions of ordinary differential equations to illustrate the basic procedure.

The first task is to derive suitable computing equations from the set of differential equations presented, as illustrated in Chapter 2. An alternative method of introducing amplitude scale factors is described in Section 3.6. The derivation of suitable computing equations is based on the approximate assessment of the highest problem frequencies and the maximum values of variables.

3.2 CHOICE OF TIME SCALE FACTOR

The choice of time scale factors is dictated by several considerations which may be classified as the following:

(i) The highest computational frequency should be well within the dynamic capability of those computing units with the poorest response. For example, if electromechanical units are employed for function generation these dictate the highest problem frequency. Alternatively the recording equipment to be used may limit the upper frequency limit.

If the problem frequency is too high, taking into account the above considerations, excessive phase errors will occur which, in general, will result in significant dynamic computing errors.

(ii) The maximum computing period is also restricted since integrator errors are time dependent and after a certain period such errors reach significant proportions. Moreover, integrators with large time constants, which produce slowly varying outputs, are usually associated with relatively small input voltages and low potentiometer settings. This is another disadvantage since the accuracy of setting coefficients may be impaired. We see, therefore, that there is a desired range of operating frequencies for any computer installation and the time scale factor should be chosen, if possible, to meet this requirement. To achieve this aim, it would be an advantage to have approximate methods of assessing the highest frequency which occurs in the solution of the problem to be solved. Such methods are available for second order differential equations and, to some extent, for third order equations. The assessment of approximate frequencies in higher order equations generally results in a more involved procedure and, in such cases, the operator may prefer to have a trial computer run. As a result of the latter all integrator time constants can, if necessary, be altered by the required factor to give problem frequencies within the desired range. Before discussing this aspect we will consider a method for determining the approximate frequency of a set of low order differential equations.

Methods for Assessing Approximate Frequencies

Two assumptions are made to simplify the form of equations:

(i) All cross coupling terms are ignored. This assumption converts a set of n simultaneous differential equations into n separate differential equations. We can then treat each equation separately in an attempt to find its highest frequency mode.

(ii) If the equations are non-linear a quasi-linear procedure is adopted and a nominal operating point is chosen, if possible, so that small perturbations

51

of the independent variable about this point result in the maximum rate of deviation of the dependent variable.

To illustrate this procedure, consider the equations

Example 3.1

$$
\left.
\begin{aligned}
\frac{d^2x}{dt^2} + 2x - \frac{dy}{dt} &= 1 \\[2mm]
\frac{d^2y}{dt^2} + 2y + \frac{dx}{dt} &= x_0
\end{aligned}
\right\}
\tag{3.1}
$$

with zero initial conditions.

Ignore cross coupling terms

Simplified equations

$$
\left.
\begin{aligned}
\frac{d^2x}{dt^2} + 2x &= 1 \\[2mm]
\frac{d^2y}{dt^2} + 2y &= x_0
\end{aligned}
\right\}
\tag{3.2}
$$

The undamped natural radian frequency for both x and y modes is, therefore, $\sqrt{2}\,\text{rad/s}$. The correct solution is

$$
\left.
\begin{aligned}
x &= \frac{1}{2} - \frac{1}{6}\cos 2t - \frac{1}{3}\cos t - \frac{1}{6}x_0 \sin 2t + \frac{1}{3}x_0 \sin t \\[2mm]
y &= \frac{x_0}{2} - \frac{x_0}{6}\cos 2t - \frac{x_0}{3}\cos t + \frac{1}{6}\sin 2t - \frac{1}{3}\sin t
\end{aligned}
\right\}
\tag{3.3}
$$

i.e. the highest frequency in both modes is $2\,\text{rad/s}$. We see, therefore, that our approximate figure of $\sqrt{2}\,\text{rad/s}$ is a reasonably good approximation. In general, we should expect to be within the correct decade of frequency, using this approach.

Example 3.2

Linear equation with coefficients which are a function of the independent variable—Legendre's Equation

i.e.
$$
(1-x^2)\frac{d^2y}{dx^2} - 2x\frac{dy}{dx} + n(n+1)y = 0
\tag{3.4}
$$

with
$$
n = 6 \quad y(0) = -\tfrac{5}{16} \quad \frac{dy}{dx}(0) = 0
$$

We assume that our interest is confined to the range $0 \leq x \leq 1$ and $-1 \leq y \leq 1$. An approximate assessment of frequency may be obtained by considering the simplified equation for $x \to 0$

i.e.
$$\frac{d^2y}{dx^2} + 42y = 0$$

which gives the solution
$$y = -\tfrac{5}{16}\cos\omega x$$
(3.5)

where
$$\omega = \sqrt{42}\,\text{radian per unit of } x$$

The correct solution[1] is given by

$$y = \tfrac{5}{16}(46{\cdot}2x^6 - 63x^4 + 21x^2 - 1)$$
(3.6)

If we express the approximate solution with $\cos\omega x$ expressed as a power series

$$y = \tfrac{5}{16}(102{\cdot}9x^6 - 73{\cdot}5x^4 + 21x^2 - 1)$$
(3.7)

If we compare equations (3.7) and (3.6) we observe that the approximate solution is fairly good for $x < 1$ and is certainly of sufficient accuracy for scaling purposes.

Example 3.3

Non-linear example—Van der Pol's Equation[2]

$$\frac{d^2x}{dt^2} - g(1 - x^2)\frac{dx}{dt} + x = 0$$
(3.8)

where g is constant and $x(0) = K$, $\dfrac{dx}{dt}(0) = 0$

This equation describes the dynamic performance of a second order system with a non-linear damping term which gives a negative value for low values of x and a positive value for $x > 1$.

For values of x approaching zero the approximate equation is given by

$$\frac{d^2x}{dt^2} - g\frac{dx}{dt} + x = 0$$

with a solution for $g = 0{\cdot}1$ and $K = 2$
of
$$x \simeq Ke^{0{\cdot}05t}(\cos t - 0{\cdot}05\sin t)$$
(3.9)

The approximate solution given by McLachlan[2] for $g = 0.1$ is

$$x = 2 \sin t + 0.025(\cos t - \cos 3t) + \tfrac{0.01}{16}(3 \sin t - \tfrac{5}{6} \sin 5t) \qquad (3.10)$$

This solution of course involves the higher harmonic terms but these are of small magnitude compared with the fundamental. Thus we see that our approximate solution, equation (3.9), is satisfactory as a basis for choosing our initial value of time scale factor.

These three examples illustrate the approximate method of assessing problem frequencies. In certain applications it may not be obvious how to simplify the equation to give a reasonable figure. For such cases, as already stated, an initial trial computer run will indicate the required time scale factor.

3.3 CHOICE OF AMPLITUDE SCALE FACTORS

Each amplitude scale factor has to be chosen so that the computer voltage representing each variable does not exceed the maximum operating voltage of the computing unit, usually $\pm 100\,$V. On the other hand, we do not want too small a voltage representing a variable as this would result in a poor signal to noise ratio, i.e. if the voltage is low the imperfections of the computing unit become a more significant proportion of the output voltage. It is therefore desirable to aim for a voltage, representing the maximum excursion of a problem variable, to be approximately one-half of the maximum linear range of the computing unit. This allows a factor of safety since the maximum value of each problem variable will, in general, not be known to a high degree of accuracy.

Estimates of the magnitudes of problem variables may be made from a knowledge of the physical systems represented or in some cases directly from the equations.

If we again consider equation (3.1) we may assess the mean bounded values of x and y (if they exist) for $t \to \infty$, i.e. the steady state mean levels. We have

$$\frac{d^2x}{dt^2} + 2x - \frac{dy}{dt} = 1$$

$$\frac{d^2y}{dt^2} + 2y + \frac{dx}{dt} = x_0$$

The mean value of x as $t \to \infty$ is given by $\bar{x} = \tfrac{1}{2}$. The mean value of y as $t \to \infty$ is given by $\bar{y} = x_0/2$ where it is assumed that the mean value of all derivatives go to zero at $t \to \infty$. From the approximate equation (3.2) we have already determined that the approximate value of the highest undamped natural radian frequency is $\omega_n = \sqrt{2}\,\text{rad/s}$. We may therefore guess approximate solutions of the forms

$$x = \tfrac{1}{2}(1 - \cos\omega_n t) \qquad \frac{dx}{dt} = \tfrac{1}{2}\omega_n \sin\omega_n t \qquad \frac{d^2x}{dt^2} = \tfrac{1}{2}\omega_n^2 \cos\omega_n t$$

$$y = \frac{x_0}{2}(1 - \cos\omega_n t) \qquad \frac{dx}{dt} = \frac{x_0}{2}\omega_n \sin\omega_n t \qquad \frac{d^2x}{dt^2} = \frac{x_0}{2}\omega_n^2 \cos\omega_n t$$

giving maximum values

$$\left.\begin{array}{llll}
x\big|_{\max} = 1 & \left.\dfrac{dx}{dt}\right|_{\max} = \dfrac{\omega_n}{2}x\Big|_{\max} & \left.\dfrac{d^2x}{dt^2}\right|_{\max} = \omega_n \dfrac{dx}{dt}\Big|_{\max} \\[3mm]
y\big|_{\max} = x_0 & \left.\dfrac{dy}{dt}\right|_{\max} = \dfrac{\omega_n}{2}y\Big|_{\max} & \left.\dfrac{d^2y}{dt^2}\right|_{\max} = \omega_n \dfrac{dy}{dt}\Big|_{\max}
\end{array}\right\} \qquad (3.11)$$

Denoting amplitude scale factors

$$V_{x,0} = a_{x,0}\,x \qquad V_{x,1} = a_{x,1}\frac{dx}{dt} \qquad V_{x,2} = a_{x,2}\frac{d^2x}{dt^2}$$

$$V_{y,0} = a_{y,0}\,y \qquad V_{y,1} = a_{y,1}\frac{dy}{dt} \qquad V_{y,2} = a_{y,2}\frac{d^2y}{dt^2}$$

we wish to satisfy the relationships

$$\left.\begin{array}{l}
{}_{x,0}\big|_{\max} = V_{x,1}\big|_{\max} = V_{x,2}\big|_{\max} \\[2mm]
V_{y,0}\big|_{\max} = V_{y,1}\big|_{\max} = V_{y,2}\big|_{\max}
\end{array}\right\} \qquad (3.12)$$

Thus if $V_{x,0}$ and $V_{y,0}$ are properly scaled so that they do not exceed the maximum amplitude range of the respective integrators, the remaining scale factors may be derived.

For example if
$$V_{x,0}\big|_{\max} = V_{x,1}\big|_{\max}$$

$$a_{x,0}\,x_{\max} = a_{x,1}\frac{\omega_n}{2}x_{\max}$$

Therefore
$$a_{x,1} = \frac{2}{\omega_n}a_{x,0}$$

also for
$$V_{x,1}\big|_{max} = V_{x,2}\big|_{max}$$

$$a_{x,1}\frac{dx}{dt}\bigg|_{max} = a_{x,2}\frac{d^2x}{dt^2}\bigg|_{max}$$

i.e.
$$a_{x,1}\frac{dx}{dt}\bigg|_{max} = a_{x,2}\,\omega_n\frac{dx}{dt}\bigg|_{max}$$

i.e.
$$a_{x,2} = \frac{1}{\omega_n}a_{x,1}$$

Similar relationships may be derived for the variable y. This approach is valid if the solutions have a lightly damped oscillatory form. If a heavily damped solution is estimated with small overshoot we may choose the amplitude scale factors to be equal as a first trial.

For the problem above with $x_0 = 1$ we may choose an amplitude scale factor for the right-hand side terms (i.e. the forcing function) to be say 50 if the maximum range of the computing units is ± 100 V.

The approximate estimated value of ω_n is $\sqrt{2}$ rad/s. However in selecting scale factors, for computational ease, we would choose integer values. Hence suitable values for the scale factors would be:

$$\left.\begin{array}{lll} a_{x,0} = 50 & a_{x,1} = a_{x,0} & a_{x,2} = \tfrac{1}{2}a_{x,1} \\ a_{y,0} = 50 & a_{y,1} = a_{y,0} & a_{y,2} = \tfrac{1}{2}a_{y,1} \end{array}\right\} \qquad (3.13)$$

where ω_n has been chosen to be the nearest integer value, i.e. 2. An interesting empirical method (The Equal Coefficient Rule) is suggested by Jackson[3] for determining maximum amplitude values for an ordinary linear differential equation of nth order. Consider the equation

$$\frac{dx^4}{dt^4} + 70{\cdot}1\frac{d^3x}{dt^3} + 1232\frac{d^2x}{dt^2} + 1870\frac{dx}{dt} + 30{,}000x = 15{,}000u_0(t) \quad (3.14)$$

with all initial conditions zero and where $u_0(t)$ represents unit step function defined as

$$u_0(t) = \begin{array}{l} 0 \text{ for } t < 0 \\ 1 \text{ for } t > 0 \end{array}$$

On the assumption that a lightly damped mode exists we may assess x_{max} as twice the final mean value,

i.e.
$$x_{max} = 2 \times \frac{15{,}000}{30{,}000} = 1$$

To find the remaining maximum values the rule states that we divide the equation by the factor 15,000 to make the right-hand side unity and then arrange the equation so that all coefficients approximate to unity with the exception of the coefficient of x which will be 2, i.e. the above equation is now written in the form

$$\left(\frac{1}{15{,}000}\frac{dx^4}{dt^4}\right)+0{\cdot}938\left(\frac{1}{200}\frac{dx^3}{dt^3}\right)+0{\cdot}986\left(\frac{1}{12}\frac{dx^2}{dt^2}\right)$$
$$+0{\cdot}623\left(\frac{1}{5}\frac{dx}{dt}\right)+2\left(\frac{x}{1}\right)=u_0(t) \tag{3.15}$$

The reciprocal of the numerical factor inside each bracket represents the approximate maximum value of the respective variable. Thus from above

$$\left.\frac{dx^4}{dt^4}\right|_{\max}\simeq 15{,}000;\quad \left.\frac{dx^3}{dt^3}\right|_{\max}\simeq 200;\quad \left.\frac{dx^2}{dt^2}\right|_{\max}\simeq 12;\quad \left.\frac{dx}{dt}\right|_{\max}\simeq 5$$

The calculated values are:

$$\left.\frac{dx^4}{dt^4}\right|_{\max}=15{,}000;\quad \left.\frac{d^3x}{dt^3}\right|_{\max}=180;\quad \left.\frac{d^2x}{dt^2}\right|_{\max}=10{\cdot}8$$
$$\left.\frac{dx}{dt}\right|_{\max}=3{\cdot}4;\quad x\big|_{\max}=0{\cdot}9$$

The estimated values are surprisingly close to the correct values. The validity of this rule has not been proved but its application to several examples is discussed in Reference 3 where it is demonstrated that the estimated values are modified if all initial conditions are not zero.

For more complicated problems, as already stated, we may make reasonable estimates of the maximum values of variables of the problem from a knowledge of the physical system being represented. Although there is no common direct method of determining these values, a careful study of probable maximum variations pays dividends, particularly in non-linear problems, in arriving at reasonable scale factors. We shall now discuss a few examples to illustrate the basic approach.

3.4 THE COMPLETE PROGRAMMING OF SPECIFIC EXAMPLES

Example 3.1 of Section 3.2

$$\frac{d^2x}{dt^2}+2x-\frac{dy}{dt}=1$$
$$\frac{d^2y}{dt^2}+2y+\frac{dx}{dt}=1$$

with zero initial conditions, and $x_0 = 1$.

Time Scale Factor

Our approximate assessment of the highest problem frequency [see equation (3.2)] is $\sqrt{2}\,\text{rad/s}$. Assume that we wish to speed up the solution by a factor of 10

i.e. $$\lambda = a_\lambda t$$

where $$a_\lambda = 0 \cdot 1 \tag{3.16}$$

From equation (3.13) we have the amplitude scale factors

$$a_{x,0} = a_{x,1} = 50 \quad a_{x,2} = 25$$

$$a_{y,0} = a_{y,1} = 50 \quad a_{y,2} = 25$$

The computing equations are

$$\frac{V_{x,2}}{a_{x,2}} + 2\frac{V_{x,0}}{a_{x,0}} - \frac{V_{y,1}}{a_{y,1}} = 1$$

$$\frac{V_{y,2}}{a_{y,2}} + 2\frac{V_{y,0}}{a_{y,0}} + \frac{V_{x,1}}{a_{x,1}} = 1$$

i.e. $$V_{x,2} = -a_{x,2}\left(\frac{2V_{x,0}}{a_{x,0}} - \frac{V_{y,1}}{a_{y,1}} - 1\right)$$

$$V_{y,2} = -a_{y,2}\left(\frac{2V_{y,0}}{a_{y,0}} + \frac{V_{x,1}}{a_{x,1}} - 1\right)$$

and inserting values we have

$$\left.\begin{array}{l} V_{x,2} = -(V_{x,0} - \tfrac{1}{2}V_{y,1} - 25) \\ V_{y,2} = -(V_{y,0} + \tfrac{1}{2}V_{x,1} - 25) \end{array}\right\} \tag{3.17}$$

with zero initial conditions. If solutions for $V_{x,2}$ and $V_{y,2}$ are not required, we may write the equations

$$-V_{x,1} = -\frac{1}{T_{x,2}}\int V_{x,2}\,d\lambda = +\frac{a_{x,2}}{T_{x,2}}\int\left(\frac{2V_{x,0}}{a_{x,0}} - \frac{V_{y,1}}{a_{y,1}} - 1\right)d\lambda$$

$$-V_{y,1} = -\frac{1}{T_{y,2}}\int V_{y,2}\,d\lambda = +\frac{a_{y,2}}{T_{y,2}}\int\left(\frac{2V_{y,0}}{a_{y,0}} + \frac{V_{x,1}}{a_{x,1}} - 1\right)d\lambda$$

where $T_{x,2}$ and $T_{y,2}$ are the respective integrator time constants. Inserting values

$$+V_{x,1} = -\frac{1}{T_{x,2}} \int (V_{x,0} - \tfrac{1}{2}V_{y,1} - 25)\,d\lambda \left.\begin{array}{c} \\ \\ \end{array}\right\}$$

$$+V_{y,1} = -\frac{1}{T_{y,2}} \int (V_{y,0} + \tfrac{1}{2}V_{x,1} - 25)\,d\lambda$$

(3.18)

The computing diagram for equation (3.17) is shown in Fig. 3.1 (a) and that for equation (3.18) is shown in Fig. 3.1 (b).

Evaluation of Time Constants of Integrator

$$V_{x,1} = \frac{1}{T_{x,2}} \int V_{x,2}\,d\lambda$$

i.e.

$$a_{x,1}a_\lambda \frac{dx}{d\lambda} = \frac{1}{T_{x,2}} \int a_{x,2}a_\lambda^2 \frac{d^2x}{d\lambda^2}\,d\lambda = \frac{a_{x,2}a_\lambda^2 dx}{T_{x,2}}\frac{dx}{d\lambda}$$

assuming zero initial conditions

i.e.

$$T_{x,2} = \frac{a_{x,2}a_\lambda}{a_{x,1}}$$

(3.19)

As described in Chapter 2, equation (2.9), the general relationship is

$$\frac{1}{K_{x,r}} = T_{x,r} = \frac{a_{x,r}a_\lambda}{a_{x,r-1}}$$

(3.20)

For our specific problem we have the following time constants

$$T_{x,1} = \frac{a_{x,1}}{a_{x,0}}a_\lambda = 0\cdot1\,\text{s}; \quad T_{x,2} = \frac{a_{x,2}}{a_{x,1}}a_\lambda = 0\cdot05\,\text{s} \left.\begin{array}{c} \\ \\ \\ \end{array}\right\}$$

$$T_{y,1} = \frac{a_{y,1}}{a_{y,0}}a_\lambda = 0\cdot1\,\text{s}; \quad T_{y,2} = \frac{a_{y,2}}{a_{y,1}}a_\lambda = 0\cdot05\,\text{s}$$

(3.21)

Note: If the factor $a_{x,r}a_\lambda/a_{x,r-1}$, for the general case is not a convenient value for the product $R_{x,r}C_{x,r}$, i.e. product of the 'rth' integrator resistor and capacitor values, we may express

$$T_{x,r} = \frac{a_{x,r}a_\lambda\alpha}{a_{x,r-1}} \quad \text{with } \alpha \leq 1$$

(3.22)

if the input to the integrator is now scaled by a potentiometer to be $\alpha V_{x,r}$.

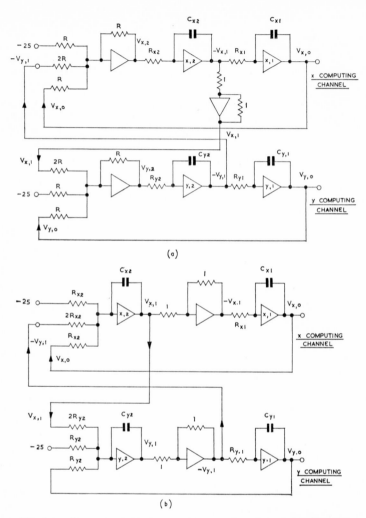

Fig. 3.1 *Alternative computing arrangements for solution of problem* 3.1

$$T_{x,1} = R_{x1} C_{x1} = 0{\cdot}1 \, \text{s} \quad T_{x,2} = R_{x2} C_{x2} = 0{\cdot}05 \, \text{s}$$

$$T_{y,1} = R_{y1} C_{y1} = 0{\cdot}1 \, \text{s} \quad T_{y,2} = R_{y2} C_{y2} = 0{\cdot}05 \, \text{s}$$

Note: All initial conditions zero.

Legendre's Equation

$$(1-x^2)\frac{d^2y}{dx^2} - 2x\frac{dy}{dx} + n(n+1)y = 0$$

with $\qquad n = 6 \quad y(0) = -\tfrac{5}{16} \quad \frac{dy}{dx}(0) = 0$

As in Section 3.2 we assume that our interest is confined to the range $0 \leq x \leq 1$ and $-1 \leq y \leq 1$. From equation (3.5) we have determined the approximate highest problem frequency as $\omega = \sqrt{42}$ rad per unit of x.

If this frequency is within the desired range of the computer we may choose a unity time scale factor

i.e. $\qquad\qquad\qquad\qquad \lambda = x$

x occurs explicitly in the equation so we may represent x by a voltage given by

$$V_{x,0} = a_{x,0}\, x$$

Since the maximum value of x is 1, a suitable value for $a_{x,0}$ is 10, i.e. $V_{x,0}$ is obtained by applying $-10\,$V to the input of an integrator with a time constant of unity.

The voltage V_x applied to a second integrator, with an initial condition of 10 V and a time constant of 0·5 s gives an output voltage $10(1 - V_{x,0}^2/100)$. Denoting the remaining amplitude scale factors as

$$V_{y,2} = a_{y,2}\frac{d^2y}{dx^2} = a_{y,2}\frac{d^2y}{d\lambda^2} \quad V_{y,1} = a_{y,1}\frac{dy}{d\lambda} \quad V_{y,0} = a_{y,0}\, y$$

we have the initial conditions

$$V_{y,0}(0) = -a_{y,0}\tfrac{5}{16} \quad V_{y,1}(0) = 0$$

and the computing equation

$$\left(1 - \frac{V_{x,0}^2}{100}\right)\frac{V_{y,2}}{a_{y,2}} - \frac{2V_{x,0}}{10}\frac{V_{y,1}}{a_{y,1}} + 42\frac{V_{y,0}}{a_{y,0}} = 0$$

i.e. $\qquad V_{y,2} = -\dfrac{a_{y,2}}{\left(1 - \dfrac{V_{x,0}^2}{100}\right)}\left(-\dfrac{0\cdot 2V_{x,0}}{a_{y,1}}\dfrac{V_{y,1}}{} + \dfrac{42V_{y,0}}{a_{y,0}}\right)$ $\qquad$ (3.23)

Choice of Amplitude Scale Factors

From equation (3.5) we have the approximate solution

$$y = -\tfrac{5}{16}\cos\omega\lambda$$

i.e. $$y_{max} = \tfrac{5}{16}$$

For a 100 volt machine we may choose $a_{y,0} = 200$

i.e. $$V_{y,0}|_{max} = 62{\cdot}5\,\text{V}$$

As before, we have the relationship

$$a_{y,1} = \frac{1}{\omega}a_{y,0} \quad a_{y,2} = \frac{1}{\omega}a_{y,1}$$

Choose a convenient integer value for ω, say 10, giving

$$a_{y,1} = 0{\cdot}1a_{y,0} \quad a_{y,2} = 0{\cdot}1a_{y,1}$$

i.e. $$a_{y,1} = 20 \qquad a_{y,2} = 2$$

Determination of Time Constants

$$T_{y,1} = \frac{a_{y,1}}{a_{y,0}}a_\lambda = 0{\cdot}1\,\text{s} \quad T_{y,2} = \frac{a_{y,2}}{a_{y,1}}a_\lambda = 0{\cdot}1\,\text{s}$$

Initial Conditions

Integrator $y,2$ initial condition zero.
Integrator $y,1$ initial condition $V_{y,0}(0) = -200\tfrac{5}{16} = -62{\cdot}5\,\text{V}$.

Computing Equation

$$V_{y,2} = -\frac{2}{\left(1 - \dfrac{V_{x,0}^2}{100}\right)}\left(-\frac{0{\cdot}2V_{x,0}\,V_{y,1}}{20} + \frac{42V_{y,0}}{200}\right)$$

i.e. $$V_{y,2} = -\frac{1}{\left(1 - \dfrac{V_{x,0}^2}{100}\right)}(-0{\cdot}02V_{x,0}\,V_{y,1} + 0{\cdot}42V_{y,0})$$

The computing arrangement for the solution of this equation is shown in Fig. 3.2.

Note: Difficulty is experienced in simulating this problem as $x \to 1$ since the term $1/(1-x^2)$ approaches infinity. A method of obviating this difficulty is discussed in Section 3.7.

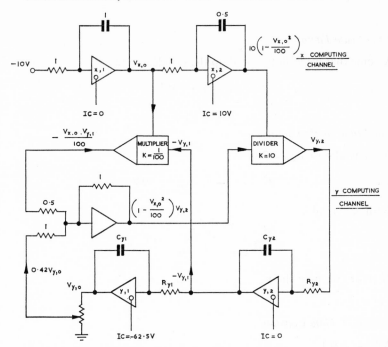

Fig. 3.2 *Solution to Legendre's equation*

$$T_{y,1} = R_{y1} \, C_{y1} = 0\cdot1\,\text{s}$$
$$T_{y,2} = R_{y2} \, C_{y2} = 0\cdot1\,\text{s}$$

Van der Pol's Equation

$$\frac{d^2x}{dt^2} - g(1-x^2)\frac{dx}{dt} + x = 0$$

where g is a constant

$$x(0) = K \qquad \frac{dx}{dt}(0) = 0$$

This equation may be transformed into the equivalent Rayleigh equation by integrating with respect to time

i.e. $$\frac{dx}{dt} - g\left(x - \frac{x^3}{3}\right) + \int x \, dt = 0 \qquad (3.25)$$

If we take the initial condition $x(0) = K = 2$ as in equation (3.9) we see that the maximum value of x is in the region of 2 units and the highest significant frequency is $1\,\text{rad/s}$.

Time Scale Factor

Assume that we wish to speed up the problem with

$$\lambda = a_\lambda t = 0 \cdot 1 t$$

Amplitude Scale Factor

We may choose $a_{x,0} = 25$

i.e. $\qquad V_{x,0}\big|_{max} = a_{x,0} x_{max} = 50\,V$

With $\omega = 1\,rad/s$

$$\frac{d^2 x}{dt^2}\bigg|_{max} = \frac{dx}{dt}\bigg|_{max} = x\big|_{max}$$

therefore we may choose $a_{x,2} = a_{x,1} = a_{x,0} = a_{x,-1} = 25$

Integrator Time Constants

With $a_\lambda = 0 \cdot 1$

$$T_{x,1} = \frac{a_{x,1}}{a_{x,0}} a_\lambda = 0 \cdot 1\,s \quad T_{x,0} = \frac{a_{x,0}}{a_{x,-1}} a_\lambda = 0 \cdot 1\,s$$

Initial Conditions

$$V_{x,1}(0) = 0 \qquad V_{x,0}(0) = a_{x,0} x(0) = 50\,V$$

Computing Equation

$$V_{x,1} = -25\left[-g\left(\frac{V_{x,0}}{25} - \frac{V_{x,0}^3}{3 \times 25^3}\right) + \int \frac{V_{x,0}}{25} \frac{d\lambda}{0 \cdot 1} \right]$$

i.e. $\qquad V_{x,1} = -\left[-g\left(V_{x,0} - \frac{V_{x,0}^3}{1875}\right) + 10\int V_{x,0}\,d\lambda \right]$ $\qquad$ (3.26)

A possible set-up is shown in Fig. 3.3 where it should be noted that the function generator has a scale factor of $1/125,000$ to ensure that it does not overload.

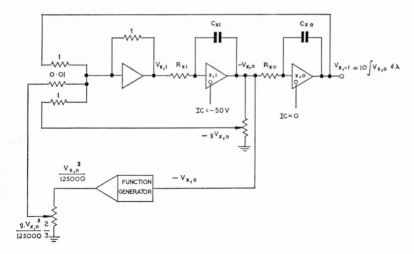

Fig. 3.3 *Solution to Van der Pol's equation*

$$T_{x,1} = C_{x1} R_{x1} = 0.1\,\text{s} \quad T_{x,0} = C_{x0} R_{x0} = 0.1\,\text{s}$$

$$\text{Constant } g \leqq 1$$

3.5 SYMBOLIC NOTATION FOR COMPUTING UNITS

The detailed computing diagrams similar to those shown in Figs. 3.1–3.3, although giving a complete picture of the components used, tend to become rather untidy for large scale problems.

It is desirable, therefore, to simplify the notation to give a less complex diagram which may be more easily understood.

Up to the present there are no internationally accepted standard symbols for analogue computing units. However there is some agreement, between computer users, for standard symbols representing the more common computing units. The symbolic notation adopted here follows the proposed I.R.E. standards for analogue computers[4] and details are given in Table 3.1.

Some additional symbols adopted in this book and not included in the I.R.E. standards are given in Chapter 5. These are necessary to indicate the mode of operation of the integrator if operated repetitively for iterative computation. This aspect is discussed in Chapter 5.

A further distinction is made, when using standard computing units, in that voltages are denoted by a capital 'V' instead of 'e' as given in Reference 4. The symbol 'e' is used to denote a voltage associated with a non-standard active network arrangement as discussed in Chapter 6.

65

3.6 AN ALTERNATIVE METHOD OF AMPLITUDE SCALING— NORMALIZED VARIABLE METHOD

An alternative to the method of amplitude scaling, which is described in Chapter 2 and the preceding sections, is called the 'normalized variable method'. In this method the computing equations are written in a form such that each computing variable is the original variable, say x, divided by its maximum value, i.e. the computing variable for x is (x/x_{max}). This (x/x_{max}) has a maximum value of unity and it may vary between $+1$ and -1 and has no dimensional units. In this way the output variables of computing units may be regarded as normalized 'per unit' quantities. For an electronic machine with a maximum amplitude range of $\pm V$ volts, the voltage $V_{x,0}$ representing the variable x may be expressed as a fraction of the maximum amplitude. In other words we may write

$$\frac{x}{x_{max}} = \frac{V_{x,0}}{V} \tag{3.27}$$

For a typical modern machine $V = 100$ and we have

$$\frac{x}{x_{max}} = \frac{V_{x,0}}{100} \tag{3.28}$$

We may therefore consider all computer variables as normalized 'per unit' variables and we do not need to express the variables as voltages. If an actual voltage value is required, then for the variable x we have

$$V_{x,0} = V\left(\frac{x}{x_{max}}\right)$$

$$= 100\left(\frac{x}{x_{max}}\right) \quad \text{for } V = 100 \tag{3.29}$$

This method is directly equivalent to the method we have adopted so far in this text where we specify dimensional scale factors. With the latter method we write

$$V_{x,0} = a_{x,0}\, x$$

The amplitude scale factor $a_{x,0}$ is chosen so that

$$V_{x,0}\mid_{max} \,\leqq\, V$$

We may therefore write

$$a_{x,0} = \frac{V}{x_{max}} \qquad (3.30)$$

i.e.

$$V_{x,0} = a_{x,0} x = V\left(\frac{x}{x_{max}}\right) \qquad (3.31)$$

which is the same result as equation (3.29). We see, therefore, that the only difference between the two methods is that in the dimensional amplitude scale factor method a variable x is represented by $V_{x,0}$ and in the normalized variable method x is represented by (x/x_{max}).

The choice of which method to adopt is one of personal preference and the reader who prefers the normalized variable method can easily rewrite the derived computing equations in this text in this alternative form.

We shall now consider one example using the normalized variable method to illustrate the approach.

Consider again Example 3.1 given by equation (3.1)

i.e.

$$\frac{d^2x}{dt^2} + 2x - \frac{dy}{dt} = 1$$

$$\frac{d^2y}{dt^2} + 2y + \frac{dx}{dt} = x_0$$

with zero initial conditions. From equation (3.11) with $\omega_n = 2$ we have

$$\left. x \right|_{max} = 1 \quad \left. \frac{dx}{dt} \right|_{max} = 1 \quad \left. \frac{d^2x}{dt^2} \right|_{max} = 2 \atop \left. y \right|_{max} = x_0 \quad \left. \frac{dy}{dt} \right|_{max} = x_0 \quad \left. \frac{d^2y}{dt^2} \right|_{max} = 2x_0 \right\} \qquad (3.32)$$

The above equations are written in the form

$$\ddot{x}_{max}\left(\frac{\ddot{x}}{\ddot{x}_{max}}\right) + 2x_{max}\left(\frac{x}{x_{max}}\right) - \dot{y}_{max}\left(\frac{\dot{y}}{\dot{y}_{max}}\right) = 1 \atop \ddot{y}_{max}\left(\frac{\ddot{y}}{\ddot{y}_{max}}\right) + 2y_{max}\left(\frac{y}{y_{max}}\right) + \dot{x}_{max}\left(\frac{\dot{x}}{\dot{x}_{max}}\right) = x_0 \right\} \qquad (3.33)$$

where

$$\dot{x} = \frac{dx}{dt} \quad \text{and} \quad \ddot{x} = \frac{d^2x}{dt^2} \text{ etc.}$$

Inserting the values from equation (3.33) we have

$$2\left(\frac{\ddot{x}}{2}\right)+2\left(\frac{x}{1}\right)-x_0\left(\frac{\dot{y}}{x_0}\right)=1$$

$$2x_0\left(\frac{\ddot{y}}{2x_0}\right)+2x_0\left(\frac{y}{x_0}\right)+\left(\frac{\dot{x}}{1}\right)=x_0$$

With $x_0 = 1$ the equation may be expressed as

$$\left(\frac{\ddot{x}}{2}\right)+\left(\frac{x}{1}\right)-0\cdot5\left(\frac{\dot{y}}{1}\right)=0\cdot5$$

$$\left(\frac{\ddot{y}}{2}\right)+\left(\frac{y}{1}\right)+0\cdot5\left(\frac{\dot{x}}{1}\right)=0\cdot5$$

i.e.

$$\left.\begin{aligned}\left(\frac{\ddot{x}}{2}\right)&=-\left[\left(\frac{x}{1}\right)-0\cdot5\left(\frac{\dot{y}}{1}\right)-0\cdot5\right]\\\left(\frac{\ddot{y}}{2}\right)&=-\left[\left(\frac{y}{1}\right)+0\cdot5\left(\frac{\dot{x}}{1}\right)-0\cdot5\right]\end{aligned}\right\}$$

(3.34)

Compare these equations with equations (3.17), to demonstrate again the equivalence of the two methods.

Note: In equation (3.17), V was effectively assumed to be 50 V, i.e. half full scale.

Evaluation of Time Constants of Integrators

As before we must remember that each integrator integrates its input variables with respect to the independent computer variable λ where $\lambda = a_\lambda t$.

From equation (3.20) we have the expression for the time constant of the 'rth' integrator in the x channel as

$$T_{x,r}=\frac{a_{x,r}\,a_\lambda}{a_{x,r-1}}=a_\lambda\frac{\left(V\left|\dfrac{d^r x}{dt_{max}^r}\right.\right)}{\left(V\left|\dfrac{d^{r-1} x}{dt_{max}^{r-1}}\right.\right)}$$

i.e.

$$T_{x,r}=a_\lambda\frac{\dfrac{d^{r-1} x}{dt_{max}^{r-1}}}{\dfrac{d^r x}{dt_{max}^r}}$$

(3.35)

where V = maximum range of the computer. Thus for our specific example

$$T_{x,1} = a_\lambda \frac{x_{max}}{\dot{x}_{max}} \quad T_{x,2} = a_\lambda \frac{\dot{x}_{max}}{\ddot{x}_{max}}$$

$$T_{y,1} = a_\lambda \frac{y_{max}}{\dot{y}_{max}} \quad T_{y,2} = a_\lambda \frac{\dot{y}_{max}}{\ddot{y}_{max}}$$

With $a_\lambda = 0.1$

$$T_{x,1} = 0.1\,\text{s} \quad T_{x,2} = 0.05\,\text{s} \quad T_{y,1} = 0.1\,\text{s} \quad T_{y,2} = 0.05\,\text{s}$$

which is the same result as before, see equation (3.21). The computing diagram to solve equation (3.34) is shown in Fig. 3.4 where the symbolic notation is used. Note this diagram is exactly equivalent to Fig. 3.1 (a).

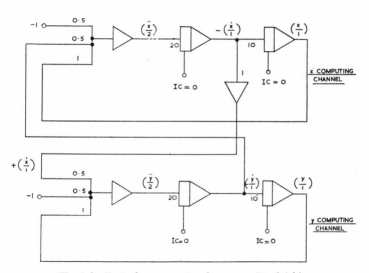

Fig. 3.4 *Equivalent computing diagram to Fig.* 3.1 (a)

Maximum computer voltage $= V = 100$ *Normalized variable scaling*

Finally on the question of amplitude scaling the reader may find in the literature variations on the two basic methods described. These other methods must obviously be equivalent to either of the two basic methods and a good discussion on this aspect is given by Jackson.[3]

3.7 USE OF TIME AS A PARAMETRIC VARIABLE TO AVOID DIVISION

In problems in which a division of functions is included there is the possibility of unbounded solutions and singularities.

For example, an equation of the form[5]

$$\frac{dy}{dx} = \frac{f(x, y)}{g(x, y)} \tag{3.36}$$

in which the division of two functions f and g is involved, the solution is unbounded when $g(x, y)$ is zero. This difficulty can be avoided by using the independent computer variable, λ, as a parameter variable in the form

$$\frac{dy}{d\lambda} = f(x, y) \quad \frac{dx}{d\lambda} = g(x, y) \tag{3.37}$$

where f and g are polynomials in x and y. The functions $x(\lambda)$ and $y(\lambda)$ are generated in the computer and may not be known explicitly. In this way if $g(x_1 y_1) = 0$ and $f(x_1 y_1) \neq 0$ the resulting singularity in dy/dx is eliminated and the graph of the solution may be continued through the point (x_1, y_1). To illustrate the procedure consider again Legendre's equation

i.e.
$$(1 - x^2)\frac{d^2 y}{dx^2} - 2x\frac{dy}{dx} + n(n+1)y = 0$$

with
$$y(0) = -\tfrac{5}{16} \quad \frac{dy}{dx}(0) = 0$$

i.e.
$$\frac{d^2 y}{dx^2} = \frac{2x\dfrac{dy}{dx} - n(n+1)y}{1 - x^2} \tag{3.38}$$

If
$$y_1 = y \quad y_2 = \frac{dy_1}{dx} = \frac{dy}{dx}$$

then
$$\frac{dy_2}{dx} = \frac{2xy_2 - n(n+1)y_1}{(1 - x^2)} = \frac{f(y_1, y_2, x)}{g(x)} \tag{3.39}$$

and
$$y_2 = \frac{dy}{dx} = \frac{dy_1}{dx} = \frac{dy_1}{d\lambda}\frac{d\lambda}{dx}$$

70

The coupled equations are:

$$\frac{dy_1}{d\lambda} = (1-x^2)y_2$$

$$\frac{dy_2}{d\lambda} = 2xy_2 - n(n+1)y_1 \qquad (3.40)$$

$$\frac{dx}{d\lambda} = 1-x^2$$

Thus no special precautions are necessary when $x^2 = 1$. For equation (3.40), we denote the following amplitude scale factors

$$V_{x,0} = a_{x,0}\,x \quad V_{x,1} = a_{x,1}\frac{dx}{d\lambda} \quad V_{y_1,0} = a_{y_1,0}\,y_1 \quad V_{y_1,1} = a_{y_1,1}\frac{dy_1}{d\lambda}$$

$$V_{y_2,0} = a_{y_2,0}\,y_2 \quad V_{y_2,1} = a_{y_2,1}\frac{dy_2}{d\lambda}$$

Now
$$\frac{dy_1}{d\lambda} = \frac{dy_1}{dx}\frac{dx}{d\lambda} \quad\text{and}\quad \frac{dy_2}{d\lambda} = \frac{dy_2}{dx}\frac{dx}{d\lambda} \qquad (3.41)$$

Since maximum value of $dx/d\lambda$ is unity, we may choose the same amplitude scale factors as used before in equation (3.23)

i.e.
$$a_{y_1,0} = a_{y,0} = 200 \quad a_{y_1,1} = a_{y,1} = 20$$

$$a_{y_2,0} = 20 \qquad\qquad a_{y_2,1} = a_{y,2} = 2$$

where $a_{y,0}$, $a_{y,1}$ and $a_{y,2}$ refer to the scale factors in equation (3.23). We may choose, as before, $a_{x,0} = a_{x,1} = 10$.

Thus
$$V_{x,1} = 10\left(1 - \frac{V_{x,0}^2}{100}\right)$$

$$V_{y_1,1} = \left(1 - \frac{V_{x,0}^2}{100}\right)V_{y_2,0} = \frac{10V_{x,1}\,V_{y_2,0}}{100}$$

$$V_{y_1,0} = \frac{1}{T_{y_1,1}}\int V_{y_1,1}\,d\lambda \quad\text{where } T_{y_1,1} = \frac{a_{y_1,1}}{a_{y_1,0}} = 0.1\,\text{s}$$

i.e.
$$V_{y_1,0} = \frac{1}{0.01}\int\left(\frac{V_{x,1}\,V_{y_2,0}}{100}\right)d\lambda$$

Also
$$V_{y_2,1} = -\left(-0.02V_{x,0}\,V_{y_2,0} + \frac{n(n+1)V_{y_1,0}}{100}\right)$$

The computing equations for $n = 6$ are given by

$$
\left.
\begin{aligned}
V_{y_1,0} &= \frac{1}{0\cdot 01} \int \left(\frac{V_{x,1} V_{y_2,0}}{100} \right) d\lambda \\
V_{y_2,1} &= -(-0\cdot 02 V_{x,0} V_{y_2,0} + 0\cdot 42 V_{y_1,0}) \\
V_{x,1} &= -10 \left(-1 + \frac{V_{x,0}^2}{100} \right)
\end{aligned}
\right\} \tag{3.42}
$$

The computing arrangement to solve these equations, using the standard notation given in Section 3.5, is shown in Fig. 3.5.

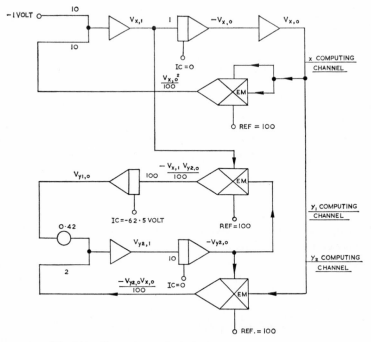

Fig. 3.5   *Alternative method of solving Legendre's equation*
(Without use of a divider)

The general case of an nth-order differential equation may be treated by considering the first canonical form of the equation, i.e. the equation

$$
\frac{d^n y}{dx^n} = y^{(n)} = \frac{f(x, y, y', \dots, y^{(n-1)})}{g(x, y, y', \dots, y^{(n-1)})} \tag{3.43}
$$

may be transformed into a set of first order equations by the transformations

i.e.
$$
\left.
\begin{aligned}
y_{i+1} &= y^i \quad \text{for } i = 0, 1, 2, ..., n \\
y &= y_1 \\
\frac{dy}{dx} &= y_2 \\
\frac{dy_i}{dx} &= y_{i+1}
\end{aligned}
\right\}
\tag{3.44}
$$

Equation (3.43) with this transformation becomes the following set of equations

$$
\frac{dy_r}{dx} = \frac{f_r(x, y_1, y_2, ..., y_n)}{g_r(x, y_1, y_2, ..., y_n)}
\tag{3.45}
$$

for $r = 1, 2, ..., n$. It is assumed that the functions f_r and g_r can be formed from the variables x, y, y_2, ..., y_n without using dividers. This assumption will not be valid for all cases, e.g. $f_1 = \sin(x/y)$. The parametric variable λ is introduced in the form

$$
\left.
\begin{aligned}
\frac{dx}{d\lambda} &= k \prod_{q=1}^{n} g_q(x, y_1, y_2, ..., y_n) \\
\frac{dy_r}{d\lambda} &= k f_r(x, y_1, y_2, ..., y_n) \prod_{q \neq r}^{n} g_q(x, y_1, y_2, ..., y_n)
\end{aligned}
\right\}
\tag{3.46}
$$

$$(k \text{ is a scaling factor})$$

such that the equations may be simulated without using dividers. The cost of this facility is that a greater number of multipliers will be required than the number of dividers required in the original formulation of the problem. For certain problems it will also be necessary to replace function generators of the independent variable λ by function generators of dependent variables.

It should be noted that this approach is valid even if the scaling factor k is itself a function of one or more variables. To cope with this situation simple step changes in k in equations (3.46) may be generated when the speed of the integrator along the trajectories is subject to wide variation.

Treatment of Unbounded Explicit Functions

We may express an unbounded function as a quotient of bounded functions. For example[6] the function $\log|z|$ can be replaced by $z \log|z|/z$ since $z \log|z|$ is bounded as z approaches zero.

73

Consider the problem of finding the definite integral

$$y = \int_0^1 \log x \, dx$$

We have
$$\frac{dy}{dx} = \log x = \frac{x \log x}{x}$$
(3.47)

If
$$z = x \log x$$

then
$$\frac{dy}{dx} = \frac{z}{x}$$
(3.48)

Introducing the parametric variable λ, we have

$$\frac{dz}{d\lambda} = \left(1 + \frac{z}{x}\right)\frac{dx}{d\lambda}$$

$$\frac{dy}{d\lambda} = \frac{z}{x}\frac{dx}{d\lambda}$$
(3.49)

If
$$\frac{dx}{d\lambda} = -x$$

then
$$\frac{dy}{d\lambda} = -z$$
(3.50)

and
$$\frac{dz}{d\lambda} = -(x+z)$$

Equations (3.50) have the solution $y = \int_1^x \log x \, dx$ if initial conditions are $x_0 = 1$, $y_0 = 0$ and $z_0 = x_0 \log x_0 = 0$. For such equations, x never reaches zero, but all variables eventually become so close to zero that good results are obtained.

It should also be noted that equations (3.50) are linear.

Treatment of Unbounded Derivatives[6]

An unbounded derivative need not be generated on the computer to obtain a solution of a differential equation. For this approach we may introduce a transformation which often reduces the amount of required equipment.

Consider again Legendre's equation and introduce the transformation

$$z = \frac{dy}{dx}(1-x^2) \tag{3.51}$$

where z is now generated in the computer instead of dy/dx.

Thus
$$\left.\begin{aligned}
\frac{dz}{d\lambda} &= \frac{d^2y}{dx^2}(1-x^2)\frac{dx}{d\lambda} - 2x\frac{dy}{dx}\frac{dx}{d\lambda} \\
&= -n(n+1)y\frac{dx}{d\lambda} \text{ [from equation (3.38)]}
\end{aligned}\right\} \tag{3.52}$$

Since
$$\frac{dy}{dx} = \frac{z}{1-x^2}$$

the final set of equations is

$$\left.\begin{aligned}
\frac{dy}{d\lambda} &= z \\
\frac{dx}{d\lambda} &= 1-x^2 \\
\frac{dz}{d\lambda} &= -n(n+1)y\frac{dx}{d\lambda}
\end{aligned}\right\} \tag{3.53}$$

i.e. fewer multipliers are required than in equation (3.40). Obviously this approach cannot be used if a solution of dy/dx is required and the equations (3.40) would have to be solved for this case.

The use of transformations gives a significant advantage in problems for which the solution of the zero derivative term is bounded but higher derivatives are unbounded. The equation

$$\frac{d^2y}{dx^2} = -\frac{1+\left(\frac{dy}{dx}\right)^2}{y} \tag{3.54}$$

has a solution

$$(x+A)^2 + y^2 = B^2 \tag{3.55}$$

where A and B are constants dictated by the particular initial conditions.

This solution may be plotted on the computer by rearranging equation (3.54) as follows:

$$y\frac{d^2y}{dx^2} = -\left[1+\left(\frac{dy}{dx}\right)^2\right]$$ (3.56)

$$\int y\frac{d^2y}{dx^2}dx = -\int\left[1+\left(\frac{dy}{dx}\right)^2\right]dx$$

i.e. $$y\frac{dy}{dx} - \int\left(\frac{dy}{dx}\right)^2 dx = -x - \int\left(\frac{dy}{dx}\right)^2 dx$$

i.e. $$\frac{dy}{dx} = -\frac{x}{y}$$ (3.57)

The unscaled computing equations are therefore

$$\left.\begin{array}{l} \dfrac{dy}{d\lambda} = -x \\[2ex] \dfrac{dx}{d\lambda} = y \end{array}\right\}$$ (3.58)

The computing arrangement is similar to that for an elementary oscillator from which circles may be plotted.

This procedure again avoids difficulties associated with division and in addition the unbounded dy/dx which appears at the output of an integrator.

Example—Electron Beam Focusing[7]

The focusing of a beam of electrons in a magnetic field for a certain industrial application is described by a modification of Mathieu's equation

i.e. $$\left.\begin{array}{l} \dfrac{dr_2}{dt} = \dfrac{\alpha}{r_1} - \beta(1+\cos 2t)r_1 \\[2ex] \dfrac{dr_1}{dt} = r_2 \end{array}\right\}$$ (3.59)

where r_1 is the radial distance of the electron from the axis of the beam and α and β are variable parameters. Writing

and $$\left.\begin{array}{l} \dfrac{dr_2}{d\lambda} = \alpha - \beta r_1^2(1+\cos 2t) \\[2ex] \dfrac{dt}{d\lambda} = r_1 \end{array}\right\}$$ (3.60)

we have $$\left.\frac{dr_1}{d\lambda}\frac{d\lambda}{dt} = r_2 \quad \text{i.e.}\ \frac{dr_1}{d\lambda} = r_2 r_1\right\}$$

and these equations are suitable for simulation purposes in that division has been avoided. A physical interpretation of this problem may be described in the following manner. For large values of r_1, the electrons experience small forces and this part of the problem can be computed quickly. As the value of r_1 approaches zero, the mutual electrostatic repulsion of the Coulomb force becomes very large so that the velocity r_2

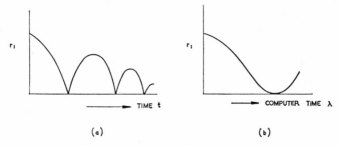

(a)   (b)

Fig. 3.6   *Electron beam focussing problem*

is reversed in a short time and distance. This part of the problem therefore needs to be computed on a slow time scale and the choice of $dt/d\lambda = r_1$ has the desired effect of slowing down the computing operation as r_1 approaches zero.

If a recording is taken of the solution r_1 the movement of the recorder in the horizontal direction is not uniform but slows down at the sharp corners where $r_1 \rightarrow 0$. The solution is illustrated in Fig. 3.6(a). For comparison purposes a plot of r_1 against computer time λ on a fixed speed recorder is shown in Fig. 3.6(b).

3.8   THE FINAL PROGRAMME

After a given set of equations has been programmed it is necessary to check the validity of the computing diagram. Probably the best method is to reconstruct the equations from the latter, preferably by a second programmer. This approach tends to ensure a standard of clarity and uniformity in nomenclature.

The next step, particularly in a large scale problem, is to compile tables listing (i) potentiometer numbers and their settings, (ii) initial conditions on integrators, (iii) time constants of integrators and their location numbers, (iv) scale factors of adders, multipliers, function generators, etc. and their location numbers, (v) time scale factor and (vi) amplitude scale factors (if these are used). In addition, for problems involving parameter perturbation analysis, which is discussed in a later chapter, a table should be compiled of the relevant potentiometers which change parameters and their range of settings.

3.9 WIRING OR PATCHING OF THE COMPUTER

With the satisfactory conclusion of the above checks the problem is ready to be patched on the computer. If the patch-board is removable the patching can be done at leisure and this tends to reduce possible errors. A good procedure is to have two operators to carry out this task. The first operator inserts the desired connections on the computer according to the instructions of the second operator, who is following the computing diagram, and who underlines each interconnection on the latter as it is made. When this procedure has been completed a final check is provided by comparing the number of connections at the input and output of each computing unit on the patch-board with those on the computing diagram. Patch-boards with a logical geometrical location of input and output sockets of units, to minimize the length and number of patch-cords, have a significant advantage for checking purposes. A practical example of a patch-board which employs only shorting pins and no patch-cords is given by the early Short Machine.[8] In the modern version of this machine a four-layer patch-board is used together with shorting pins and again no patch-cords are necessary.

With a removable patch-panel it is possible to construct an automatic device to check the interconnections and print a list of numbers which indicate the connections between various sockets. This information is then compared with the computing diagram. A practical example of such a device is described by Braun and Warshawsky.[9]

3.10 SETTING OF COEFFICIENTS, TIME CONSTANTS AND INITIAL CONDITIONS

With the patch-board connections checked, the setting of potentiometer coefficients, time constants and initial conditions may be carried out. In a modern machine the potentiometers are set by a servo-mechanism by punching a set of push buttons, usually arranged in decades, to choose the potentiometer number and a further set of buttons to choose the desired coefficients. The servo-mechanism is automatically connected to the relevant potentiometer by means of a clutch and rotates the shaft of the latter to the desired setting, which represents the input voltage to the servo-mechanism. (See Chapter 2.) A further refinement, which is an advantage on a large machine, is to feed the information into the machine by passing punched paper tape through a tape-reader. The tape-reader transmits the same information as the manually operated push buttons.

It is usual in such installations to have a printer which prints the potentio-meter number and its setting after the potentiometer has been set.

For smaller machines (of the order of 30 amplifiers) the potentiometers are usually set manually since the cost of a servo-system is not justified. For this task it is necessary to adjust each potentiometer with its load resistance connected as in the servo-set system. This means that the dial setting of the potentiometer does not give a true indication of the coefficient and it is necessary to have a bridge balance arrangement. An alternative arrangement is to use a digital voltmeter to measure the voltage at the wiper of the loaded potentiometer.

Initial conditions on integrators are usually set by one of the potentio-meters and the procedure is the same as before.

Time constants of integrators are usually set manually and preferably on the patch-board since the settings may be checked at the same time as the other interconnections. In some machines, however, push button or rotary switch selection is used.

The coefficients of other forms of computing units such as multipliers and function generators are usually set manually.

3.11 STATIC CHECKS

A static check may be made on the overall computing system by inserting arbitrary initial conditions into all integrators when switched to the initial condition or 'set' mode. Voltages appearing at the outputs of all computing units, as a result of these initial conditions, may be checked against the correct values, which may be easily evaluated since the integrators are not integrating. These checks confirm the validity of all scale factors, wiring and setting of coefficients of all units.

In a large machine an automatic checking system is usually incorporated.

3.12 INITIAL COMPUTER RUNS

With all the previous checks completed the computer may be operated for trial runs to check that suitable amplitude scaling has been used. The procedure is to check the voltage output of each computing unit to ensure that it is a reasonable value. If not, modification to the relevant scale factor will be necessary. The presence of a computing unit which is overloaded is usually indicated by a neon light but no indication is given of computing units operating with a very small signal level.

At this stage it is also necessary to check the validity of the chosen time scale factor and, if not correct, to change the time constants of all units accordingly.

On the completion of these tests the computer is ready for normal operation. The preceding checks may appear to be rather pedantic but, even in a relatively small problem set-up, bitter experience has proved the need for a rigorous and methodical procedure for patching and for checking computer operations.

A fuller description of check procedures is given by Fifer.[10]

3.19 MODERN DEVELOPMENTS IN PROGRAMMING

With the facility of coefficient setting by punched tape a logical development is to construct a complete programme code of instructions for the analogue machine which may be obtained from a digital computer.[11] An example of this approach is described by Green *et al.*[12] who describe the Apache Code which is written for the I.B.M.7090 digital computer for use with the Pace 231–R Analogue computer. For a problem involving about one hundred amplifiers on an analogue computer the instruction code development takes about 3 minutes on the I.B.M.7090 machine.

A further development is the possibility of automatic patching which may also be programmed on a digital computer. Some considerations of a simple automatic patching system are described by Miura and Iwata.[13] An earlier approach is described by Rao.[14] The main limitation on automatic patching seems to be the number of switches which are necessary to make the interconnections. With electromechanical switches the question of reliability arises and the solution may be to use solid state switches if these can be designed so that their defects in respect of leakage current and finite resistance, in the open circuit condition, have no significant effect on computational accuracy.

An investigation of analogue computing methods by digital computers is described by Hermann.[15]

These papers indicate the general trend towards the concept of controlling the analogue computer or computers from a master digital computer. With the facility of iterative operation, which involves storage, on the analogue computer (see Chapter 5), it seems reasonable to place the control of the analogue machine under the digital computer. In this way calculations of an arithmetical nature, decision logic, memory storage, etc. may be determined in the digital machine and the analogue machine may be used to perform the necessary high speed calculations. In other words, the aim is to get the optimum results from both machines.

Although these developments appear to be logical for large machines involving the setting of a large number of coefficients, it will be necessary to ensure that the engineer user is not presented with an automatic monster which does not permit him to have a physical appreciation of the problem.

REFERENCES

1. A. BRONWELL: *Advanced Mathematics in Physics and Engineering* (McGraw-Hill, 1953).

2. N. W. MCLACHLAN: *Ordinary Non-Linear Differential Equations* (Oxford University Press, 1950).

3. A. S. JACKSON: *Analog Computation*, Chapter 3 (McGraw-Hill, 1930).

4. A. S. JACKSON: 'Proposed I.R.E. Standards for Analog Computers', *I.R.E. Transactions on Electronic Computers*, 1962, EC-11, **1**, pp. 67–79.

5. M. E. FISHER: 'Avoiding the Need for Dividing Units in Setting Up Differential Analysers', *J. Sci. Instrum.*, 1957, **34**, pp. 334–5.

6. A. HAUSNER: 'Parametric Techniques for Eliminating Division and Treating Singularities in Computer Solutions of Ordinary Differential Equations', *I.R.E. Trans. on Electronic Computers*, 1962, EC-H, **1**, pp. 42–5.

7. D. A. EYEIONS: 'Variable Time Scaling', The General Electric Co. Ltd., Computer Unit Report No. CU27, 1962.

8. R. J. A. PAUL: 'The Short Electronic Analogue Computer', *The Overseas Engineer*, 1956, XXIX, **337**, pp. 205–8.

9. W. G. BRAUN and L. M. WARSHAWSKY: 'Verifier Prints Out Patch-board Locations', *Control Engineering*, 1955, **2**, pp. 83–5.

10. S. FIFER: *Analogue Computation*, Vol. 2 (McGraw-Hill, 1961).

11. R. J. A. PAUL: 'Combined Analogue/digital Techniques and Automatic Programming', *Proceedings of the Third International Analogue Computation Meeting, Opatija, Yugslavia, 1961*, pp. 19–23 (Presses Academique Europeennes, Bruxelles, 1962).

12. C. GREEN *et al.*: 'Le Code Apache', *ibid.*, pp. 441–55.

13. T. MIURA and J. IWATA: 'Analogue Computer Automatic Programming Systems', *ibid.*, pp. 464–74.

14. R. N. RAO: 'Logical Design of an Analogue Computer Patching System using Punched Tape Setting-up Data', College of Aeronautics Thesis, 1960.

15. H. HERMANN: 'On the Simulation of Analog Computing Methods by Digital Computers', Reference 13, pp. 478–91.

Chapter 4

DYNAMIC ANALOGIES AND NETWORK ELEMENT TRANSFORMS

4.1 INTRODUCTION

AS ALREADY MENTIONED, DYNAMIC ANALOGY IS THE REPRESENTATION of one physical model by another model of different physical form, with the conditions imposed that the mathematical relationship describing the dynamic performance in both systems should be identical.

The use of this concept has proved to be very valuable, since the behaviour of certain physical systems may be studied by investigating the behaviour of an analogous system, which may be constructed more easily.

Historically, electrical systems were studied by investigating the behaviour of the analogous mechanical systems and this approach has resulted in many comprehensive mechanical models.[1,2,3] However, in 1925 Nickle[4] discussed the applications of electrical circuits to the solutions of dynamics and, since this time, the procedure has developed extensively due to the ease of constructing analogous electrical systems.[5]

A consistent theory for constructing analogous networks is due to such workers as Firestone[6] and Trent.[7] The method of construction is based on the fundamental concepts of a potential (across) variable and a flow (through) variable in dynamics. These concepts may be applied to continuous element and discrete element systems but attention will be confined in this chapter to a consideration of the latter. The reader is referred to the work of Karplus[8] for a description of field problem applications.

To indicate how analogous networks are derived, we will now consider the properties of the ideal discrete network elements in dynamics, with particular reference to electrical and mechanical systems. Acoustical elements are discussed in some detail in Reference 9.

4.2 VARIABLES IN DYNAMICS

Potential or Across Variable $[\alpha(t)]$

This is a variable whose value must be specified with respect to its value at some other point in the system. Thus we have voltage in the electrical system since it specifies the difference in potential between two points.

Similarly we have velocity in the mechanical system, since velocity is measured with respect to some point and hence is really the velocity difference between two points.

Thus we say that $e(t)$ is analogous to $\omega(t)$.

The generalized potential is written as $\alpha(t)$.

Flow or Through Variable $\beta(t)$

The value of this variable is obtained by measuring the flow through a point without reference to any other point.

In the electrical system current is a flow variable which can be measured by the insertion of an ammeter at the point under consideration.

Force in the mechanical translational system or torque in the mechanical rotational system are also flow variables which can be measured by the insertion of, say, a spring balance.

Thus we say that $i(t)$ is analogous to $f(t)$.

The generalized flow variable is written as $\beta(t)$.

The concept of the generalized potential variable $\alpha(t)$ and the generalized flow variable $\beta(t)$ may be applied to all physical systems and some examples are given in Table 4.1.[8]

TABLE 4.1

Branch of Physics	Potential or Across Variable $\alpha(t)$	Flow or Through Variable $\beta(t)$
Electrodynamics	Voltage	Current
Electrostatics	Electric Potential	Flux
Magnetics	Potential m.m.f.	Flux
Electromagnetics	Potential E.M.	Flux
Statics (mechanical)	Displacement	Force or Torque
Dynamics (mechanical)	Displacement or Velocity	Force or Torque
Elasticity	Strain	Stress
Fluid Mechanics	Velocity Potential (pressure)	Flow Rate
Particle Diffusion	Concentration	Mass Transfer Rate
Heat Transfer	Temperature	Heat Flux

We may now construct a table showing the equivalence between corresponding elements in electrical and mechanical systems.

The correspondence between mathematical relationships in the two systems is demonstrated in the later sections. This equivalence is summarized in Table 4.2.

TABLE 4.2

Quantity	Electrical	Mechanical	
		Rectilinear	Rotational
Parameters	Capacitance	Mass	Polar moment of inertia
	Conductance	Viscous Friction Coefficient	Viscous Friction Coefficient
	Reciprocal of Self Inductance	Spring Constant	Spring Constant
Potential Variable	Potential Difference or Voltage	Linear Velocity or Displacement	Angular Velocity or Displacement
Flow Variable	Current	Force	Torque

4.3 IDEAL LINEAR DISCRETE ELEMENTS IN DYNAMICS

There are two basic types of element which are assumed to be time invariant elements, i.e. energy dissipation and energy storage or reservoir elements. In addition we employ the concepts of ideal energy sources and ideal energy transfer and gyration.

We will now consider these elements for electrical and mechanical systems.

4.3.1 Energy Dissipation

The bi-lateral elements for the two systems are represented in Table 4.3. A bi-lateral element is defined as one in which the flow variable may be directed towards either end point. It should be noted that discrete variable values may only be established at the points of the bi-lateral elements.

TABLE 4.3

Electrical	Mechanical	
	Rectilinear	*Rotational*
resistance	viscous friction or viscous friction	viscous friction or viscous friction
$e_R(t) \underset{=}{\triangle}$ applied voltage $i_R(t) \underset{=}{\triangle}$ current flowing $R \underset{=}{\triangle}$ resistance $G \underset{=}{\triangle} \dfrac{1}{R} \underset{=}{\triangle}$ conductance	$\omega_a(t) \underset{=}{\triangle}$ linear velocity $f_a(t) \underset{=}{\triangle}$ force $a \underset{=}{\triangle}$ viscous friction coefficient	$\omega_b(t) \underset{=}{\triangle}$ angular velocity $f_b(t) \underset{=}{\triangle}$ torque $b \underset{=}{\triangle}$ viscous friction coefficient

We have the following relationships

$$\left.\begin{array}{lll} e_R(t) = R i_R(t) & \omega_a(t) = \dfrac{1}{a} f_a(t) & \omega_b(t) = \dfrac{1}{b} f_b(t) \\[2mm] i_R(t) = G v_R(t) & f_a(t) = a\omega_a(t) & f_b(t) = b\omega_b(t) \end{array}\right\} \quad (4.1)$$

Also denoting power dissipation by $P(t)$ and energy dissipation by $W(t)$ we have

$$\left.\begin{array}{lll} P_R(t) = e_R(t)i_R(t) & P_a(t) = \omega_a(t)f_a(t) & P_b(t) = \omega_b(t)f_b(t) \\[2mm] \quad = R i_R(t)^2 & \quad = \dfrac{1}{a}f_a(t)^2 & \quad = \dfrac{1}{b}f_b(t)^2 \\[2mm] \quad = G e_R(t)^2 & \quad = a\omega_a(t)^2 & \quad = b\omega_b(t)^2 \end{array}\right\} \quad (4.2)$$

$$\left.\begin{array}{lll} W_R(t) = \displaystyle\int_{-\infty}^{t} P_R(t)\,dt & W_a(t) = \displaystyle\int_{-\infty}^{t} P_a(t)\,dt & W_b(t) = \displaystyle\int_{-\infty}^{t} P_b(t)\,dt \\[4mm] \quad = R \displaystyle\int_{-\infty}^{t} i_R(t)^2\,dt & \quad = \dfrac{1}{a}\displaystyle\int_{-\infty}^{t} f_a(t)^2\,dt & \quad = \dfrac{1}{b}\displaystyle\int_{-\infty}^{t} f_b(t)^2\,dt \\[4mm] \quad = G \displaystyle\int_{-\infty}^{t} e_R(t)^2\,dt & \quad = a \displaystyle\int_{-\infty}^{t} \omega_a(t)^2\,dt & \quad = b \displaystyle\int_{-\infty}^{t} \omega_b(t)^2\,dt \end{array}\right\}$$
$$(4.3)$$

4.3.2 Energy Storage or Reservoir

In a generalized dynamic system containing an ideal discrete time-invariant storage element λ_c, which is equivalent to mass in a mechanical system or capacitance in an electrical system, we have

$$\alpha(t) = \frac{1}{\lambda_c} \int_{-\infty}^{t} \beta(t)\,dt$$

or

$$\beta(t) = \lambda_c \frac{d}{dt}\alpha(t)$$

(4.4)

where $\alpha(t)$ and $\beta(t)$ are defined in the range $-\infty \leq t \leq \infty$.

In the analysis of a physical system we are generally interested in the response of the system to the application of an excitation or disturbance. For convenience the instant at which the excitation or disturbance takes place is called the reference time, which we denote as $t = 0$. This concept of reference time introduces the need for initial conditions.

We may restrict the range of the variables $\alpha(t)$ and $\beta(t)$ respectively as $0 < t \leq \infty$ by multiplying them by the unit step function $\mu_0(t)$ (see Appendix A.1).

Thus the function $\mu_0(t)\alpha(t)$ is defined as follows:

$$\mu_0(t)\alpha(t) = 0 \qquad \text{for } t \leq 0$$

$$\mu_0(t)\alpha(t) = \alpha(t) \quad \text{for } t \geq 0^+$$

(4.5)

$$\mu_0(t)\alpha(t), \text{ undefined in range } 0 < t < 0^+$$

where $t = 0^+$ is defined as the limiting value of t as t approaches the origin along the positive time axis. Thus for equation (4.4)

$$\mu_0(t)\alpha(t) = \frac{\mu_0(t)}{\lambda_c} \int_{-\infty}^{t} \beta(t)\,dt$$

$$= \frac{\mu_0(t)}{\lambda_c} \int_{-\infty}^{0} \beta(t)\,dt + \frac{\mu_0(t)}{\lambda_c} \int_{0}^{t} \beta(t)\,dt$$

i.e.

$$\mu_0(t)\alpha(t) = \mu_0(t)\alpha(0) + \frac{\mu_0(t)}{\lambda_c} \int_{0}^{t} \beta(t)\,dt$$

or

$$\mu_0(t)\alpha(t) = \alpha(0^+) + \frac{1}{\lambda_c} \int_{0^+}^{t} \beta(t)\,dt$$

(4.6)

where

$$\alpha(0) = \frac{1}{\lambda_c} \int_{-\infty}^{t} \beta(t)\,dt$$

two elements results in the coincidence of two nodes forming a single node. The term 'node' in this context has a different meaning than it has in classical dynamics where it refers to a point of zero displacement in a vibrating system.

The line segment in (b) between two nodes represents a branch of the network. Any closed path, comprising one or more branches in series, is called a loop. If all the line segments can be mapped on a plane, without crossing, the graph is called a planar graph and the corresponding network is called a planar network. Linear graph theory forms a fundamental basis for the analysis of discrete-parameter dynamic systems and is based on the rigorous discipline of topology.

However, for the limited use of two-terminal elements, the network diagram or the linear graph may be used as a basis for uniting the circuital or nodal equations and there is no significant advantage in using the graph.

For the case of multi-terminal components the linear graph does not represent the geometry of the network and takes on new and important significance.

As this chapter is confined to a discussion of two-terminal elements the network rather than the linear graph will be used. The reader is referred to References 7 and 11 for a good account of the applications of linear graph theory.

It should be noted that the concepts discussed, with reference to Fig. 4.1, also apply to all forms of linear discrete parameter networks, such as mechanical or electromechanical networks. Attention is confined in this chapter, to the consideration of networks comprising linear, time-invariant, discrete-parameter elements. The latter consist of energy coupling elements, energy gyration elements, independent energy source elements and dependent energy source elements.

A passive network is defined as one consisting of passive elements only, where the latter are regarded as those in which the energy input to them is always positive regardless of the operating conditions. Thus the energy input to a passive element during the time interval $t = 0$ to $t = T$ is defined a

$$w(t) = \int_0^T \alpha(t)\beta(t)\,dt \tag{4.8}$$

if $\alpha(t)$ and $\beta(t)$ are both zero at $t = 0$, i.e. the integral in equation (4.8) is greater than zero under all conditions of operation.

An active element is one in which equation (4.8) is not valid.

An active network is therefore defined as one containing one or more than one active element.

TABLE 4.5

Electrical	Mechanical	
	Rectilinear	Rotational

Electrical:

$L \triangleq$ self inductance
$i_L(t)$ is current (flow variable)
$e_L(t)$ is voltage (potential variable)

$$e_L(t) = L \frac{d}{dt} i_L(t)$$

$$\mu_0(t)e_L(t) = L \frac{d}{dt} i_L(t)\Big|_{t>0^+} - L i_L(0^+)\mu_1(t)$$

$$i_L(t) = \frac{1}{L}\int_{-\infty}^{t} e_L(t)\, dt$$

$$\frac{1}{L}\int_{0^+}^{t} e_L(t)\, dt + i_L(0^+)$$

Rectilinear:

$\lambda_k \triangleq$ spring compliance
$f_k(t)$ is force (flow variable)
$\omega_k(t)$ is velocity (potential variable)

$$\omega_k(t) = \lambda_k \frac{d}{dt} f_k(t)$$

$$\mu_0(t)\omega_k(t) = \lambda_k \frac{d}{dt} f_k(t)\Big|_{t>0^+} - \lambda_k f_k(0^+)\mu_1(t)$$

$$f_k(t) = \frac{1}{\lambda_k}\int_{-\infty}^{t} \omega_k(t)\, dt$$

$$\mu_0(t)f_k(t) = \frac{1}{\lambda_k}\int_{0^+}^{t} \omega_k(t)\, dt + f_k(0^+)$$

Rotational:

$\lambda_K \triangleq$ spring compliance
$f_K(t)$ is torque (flow variable)
$\omega_K(t)$ is velocity (potential variable)

$$\omega_K(t) = \lambda_K \frac{d}{dt} f_K(t)$$

$$\mu_0(t)\omega_K(t) = \lambda_K \frac{d}{dt} f_K(t)\Big|_{t>0^+} - \lambda_K f_K(0^+)\mu_1(t)$$

$$f_K(t) = \frac{1}{\lambda_K}\int_{-\infty}^{t} \omega_K(t)\, dt$$

$$\mu_0(t)f_K(t) = \frac{1}{\lambda_K}\int_{0^+}^{t} \omega_K(t)\, dt + f_K(0^+)$$

$$P_L(t) = e_L(t)i_L(t)$$
$$= L\left(\frac{d}{dt}i_L(t)\right)i_L(t)$$
$$= \frac{1}{L}e_L(t)\int_{-\infty}^{t}e_L(t)\,dt$$
$$= \frac{1}{L}\Psi(t)\frac{d}{dt}\Psi(t)$$

where $\quad \Psi(t) = \int_{-\infty}^{t}e_L(t)\,dt$
$\quad\quad\quad\quad$ = Flux Linkage

$$W_L(t) = \int_{-\infty}^{t}P_L(t)\,dt$$
$$\mu_0(t)W_L(t) = \int_{0^+}^{t}P_L(t)\,dt + W_L(0^+)$$
$$W_L(t) = \tfrac{1}{2}Li_L(t)^2 = \frac{1}{2L}\Psi(t)^2$$

$$P_k(t) = \omega_k(t)f_k(t)$$
$$= \lambda_k f_k(t)\frac{d}{dt}f_k(t)$$
$$= \frac{1}{\lambda_k}\omega_k(t)\int_{-\infty}^{t}\omega_k(t)\,dt$$
$$= \frac{1}{\lambda_k}x_k(t)\frac{d}{dt}x_k(t)$$

where $\quad x_k(t) = \int_{-\infty}^{t}\omega_k(t)\,dt$
$\quad\quad\quad\quad$ = Linear Displacement

$$W_k(t) = \int_{-\infty}^{t}P_k(t)\,dt$$
$$\mu_0(t)W_k(t) = \int_{0^+}^{t}P_k(t)\,dt + W_k(0^+)$$
$$W_k(t) = \tfrac{1}{2}\lambda_k f_k(t)^2 = \frac{1}{2\lambda_k}x_k(t)^2$$

$$P_K(t) = \omega_K(t)f_K(t)$$
$$= \lambda_K f_K(t)\frac{d}{dt}f_K(t)$$
$$= \frac{1}{\lambda_K}\omega_K(t)\int_{-\infty}^{t}\omega_K(t)\,dt$$
$$= \frac{1}{\lambda_K}\theta_K(t)\frac{d}{dt}\theta_K(t)$$

where $\quad \theta_K(t) = \int_{-\infty}^{t}\omega_K(t)\,dt$
$\quad\quad\quad\quad$ = Angular Displacement

$$W_K(t) = \int_{-\infty}^{t}P_K(t)\,dt$$
$$\mu_0(t)W_K(t) = \int_{0^+}^{t}P_K(t)\,dt + W_K(0^+)$$
$$W_K(t) = \tfrac{1}{2}\lambda_K f_K(t)^2 = \frac{1}{2\lambda_K}\theta_K(t)^2$$

4.5 IDEAL ENERGY SOURCES

We have used the concept of an ideal potential variable source and an ideal flow variable source and these are represented in Fig. 4.2.

This representation has meaning only if it is assumed that such sources are connected to finite (excluding zero) value elements. This is because the potential variable source is assumed to maintain its potential irrespective of the value of the flow variable drawn from it. Similarly the flow variable

(a)   (b)

Fig. 4.2   *Ideal energy sources*

(a) *Ideal potential variable source*   (b) *Ideal flow variable source*

source is assumed to maintain its value irrespective of the potential of the pair of terminals to which it is connected. Thus in the case of (a) a short circuit (zero resistance) across the terminal would require infinite power and in the case of (b) an open circuit (infinite resistance) would also require infinite power for the source.

The ideal elements so far considered are two-terminal elements or one-port elements. A port is defined as an accessible pair of terminals.

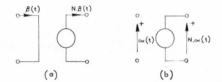

(a)   (b)

Fig. 4.3   *Ideal amplifiers*

(a) *Ideal flow variable amplifier*   (b) *Ideal potential variable amplifier*

N is a constant (*positive or negative*)

The sources considered above are termed independent energy sources. We may also have dependent energy sources in the form of any linear amplifying device having two two-terminal pairs, i.e. a two-port energy supply network such as the ideal linear concept of a transistor, a thermionic valve and electric, mechanical or hydraulic actuating devices.

We may represent such devices as shown in Fig. 4.3.

Two other alternatives are possible, i.e. a flow variable dependent potential variable source and a potential variable dependent flow variable source.

4.6 ENERGY TRANSFER AND GYRATION*

The concept of the ideal transformer two-port element is useful in the construction of networks. Examples of this concept include the ideal transformer in electric network theory and the ideal level or pair of gears in mechanical systems as illustrated in Fig. 4.4.

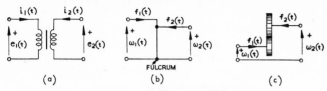

(a)   (b)   (c)

Fig. 4.4 *Ideal energy transfer elements (transformers)*

(a) *Ideal electric transformer*   (b) *Ideal rectilinear transformer (Ideal lever, small displacements)*   (c) *Ideal rotational transformer (Ideal gears)*

The generalized ideal transformer is characterized by the pair of simultaneous equations

$$\alpha_2(t) = n\alpha_1(t)$$
$$\beta_1(t) = -n\beta_2(t) \tag{4.9}$$

where n represents the transfer ratio.

Thus in (a) n is the turns ratio, in (b) n is the lever arm ratio and in (c) n is the ratio of the number of teeth on each gear. It should be noted that for case (c) in Fig. 4.4, n is negative whereas in (a) and (b) n is positive.

Another important two-port element is the ideal gyrator.[12] The gyrator may be used as an element to convert electromagnetic energy into electrostatic energy and vice-versa. A practical example of the gyrator is the ideal free gyroscope.

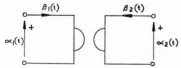

Fig. 4.5 *The generalized ideal gyrator*

The gyrator may be represented as shown in Fig. 4.5. The ideal gyrator is defined by the pair of equations

$$\alpha_1(t) = -r\beta_2(t)$$
$$\alpha_2(t) = r\beta_1(t) \tag{4.10}$$

* S. R. DEARDS: 'Fundamentals of Linear Network Theory', College of Aeronautics Lecture Supplement.

where r represents the gyrator resistance and may be positive or negative. For both the ideal transformer and gyrator the instantaneous power $P(t)$ is given by

$$P(t) = \alpha_1(t)\beta_1(t) + \alpha_2(t)\beta_2(t)$$

$$= \alpha_1(t)\beta_1(t) + n\alpha_1(t)\left[-\frac{1}{n}\beta_1(t)\right]$$

$$= 0 \text{ (transformer case)} \qquad (4.11)$$

$$= \alpha_1(t)\beta_1(t) + r\beta_1(t)\left[-\frac{1}{r}\alpha_1(t)\right]$$

$$= 0 \text{ (gyrator case)}$$

Thus no energy is dissipated or stored in the ideal transformer or gyrator. The ideal transformer transforms energy from one port to the other port without loss. The gyrator gyrates energy from one port to another without loss. Thus electromagnetic energy is converted to electrostatic energy from one port to the other port.

Practical realizations of these two ideal elements include additional one-port elements such as those already described. To illustrate this aspect consider the ideal free gyroscope whose operation is defined by the pair of equations

$$\omega_x = -\frac{F_y}{J_z \omega_z}$$

$$\omega_y = \frac{F_x}{J_z \omega_z} \qquad (4.12)$$

where ω_z is the angular velocity of the rotor about the z-axis

ω_x is the angular velocity of the rotor axis about the x-axis

ω_y is the angular velocity of the rotor axis about the y-axis

F_x is the moment about the x-axis

F_y is the moment about the y-axis

J_z is the polar moment of inertia of the rotor about its z-axis of rotation

In the ideal free gyroscope it is assumed that there is only inertia about the rotor axis.

A real gyroscope, however, will have moments of inertia about the x- and y-axes for a rotor supported in a double gymbal system in which all bearing axes are at right angles (orthogonal system). In addition the gymbal bearings will have viscous friction. The effect of the latter and the cross inertias may be considered as a mechanical load connected at each port.

Such a gyroscope may be defined by the pair of equations

$$F_x = J_x \frac{d}{dt} \omega_x + J_z \omega_z \omega_y + b_x \omega_x$$

$$F_y = J_y \frac{d}{dt} \omega_y - J_z \omega_z \omega_x + b_y \omega_y \tag{4.13}$$

where J_x is the polar moment of inertia about x-axis

J_y is the polar moment of inertia about y-axis

b_x is the viscous friction coefficient about x-axis

b_y is the viscous friction coefficient about y-axis

Consider now the arrangement shown in Fig. 4.6.

We have
$$F_{x_2} = F_x - F_{x_1} = F_x - \left(b_x \omega_x + J_x \frac{d}{dt} \omega_x \right)$$

and
$$F_{y_2} = F_y - F_{y_1} = F_y - \left(b_y \omega_y + J_y \frac{d}{dt} \omega_y \right) \tag{4.14}$$

From (4.12)
$$F_{x_2} = J_z \omega_z \omega_y$$
$$F_{y_2} = -J_z \omega_z \omega_x \tag{4.15}$$

Combining equations (4.14) and (4.15) we have the result expressed in equation (4.13) and thus the arrangement shown in Fig. 4.6 is a correct representation of the free gyroscope. The latter may be considered as an ideal gyrator to which are connected at each port the one-port elements representing viscous friction and inertia effects.

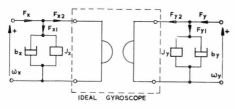

Fig. 4.6 *Free gyroscope representation*

Gyration resistance $\qquad r = \dfrac{1}{J_z \omega_z}$

4.7 DUALITY*

In the last century the French geometer J. D. Gergonne found that if the words 'point' and 'line' were interchanged in certain theorems of plane geometry, new theorems were obtained which could be proved independently. Two theorems related in this way are called dual theorems and the concepts of point and line are duals.

In 1901 Sire de Vilar[13] showed that the principle of duality applies to linear network theory. As in geometry a list of corresponding terms may be compiled and some examples are given in Table 4.6.

TABLE 4.6—DUALS FOR LINEAR, TIME-INVARIANT, DISCRETE PARAMETER SYSTEMS

Original	Symbol	Dual	Symbol
(i) *Generalized System*			
Energy	$w(t)$	Energy	$w(t)$
Power	$P(t)$	Power	$P(t)$
Potential Variable	$\alpha(t)$	Flow Variable	$\beta(t)$
Resistance of Energy Dissipation Elements	$\dfrac{\alpha(t)}{\beta(t)}$	Reciprocal of Resistance of Energy Dissipation Elements	$\dfrac{\beta(t)}{\alpha(t)}$
Energy Storage due to Elastance	$w_K(t)$	Energy Storage due to Inertia	$w_J(t)$
Polarity of Potential		Direction of Flow Variable	
Open Circuit		Short Circuit	
Time		Time	
(ii) *Electrical System*			
Voltage	$e(t)$	Current	$i(t)$
Resistance	R	Conductance	G
Inductance	L	Capacitance	C
Charge	$q(t)$	Flux Linkage	$\Psi(t)$
Electrostatic Energy	$w_c(t)$	Electromagnetic Energy	$w_L(t)$
Polarity of Voltage		Direction of Current	
(iii) *Mechanical System* (Rectilinear)			
Velocity	$\omega(t)$	Force	$f(t)$
Viscous Friction Coefficient	a	Reciprocal of Viscous Friction Coefficient	$\dfrac{1}{a}$
Spring Constant	k	Reciprocal of Mass	$\dfrac{1}{M}$
Potential Energy	$w_k(t)$	Kinetic Energy	$w_M(t)$
Polarity of Velocity		Direction of Force	

---

* S. R. DEARDS: ' Fundamentals of Linear Network Theory ', College of Aeronautics Lecture Supplement.

Examples of dual relationships are given in Tables 4.4 and 4.5

i.e.
$$\omega(t) = \frac{1}{M} \int_{-\infty}^{t} f(t)\,dt \leftrightarrow f(t) = k \int_{-\infty}^{t} \omega(t)\,dt$$

$$e(t) = \frac{1}{C} \int_{-\infty}^{t} i(t)\,dt \leftrightarrow i(t) = \frac{1}{L} \int_{-\infty}^{t} e(t)\,dt$$

4.8 NETWORK POSTULATES FOR LINEAR TIME-INVARIANT DISCRETE-PARAMETER SYSTEMS

(a) *Mechanical Systems*

Nodal Postulate

The fundamental force relationship of statics is that, for equilibrium, summation of all forces acting on a rigid body is zero.

This basic concept was used by D'Alembert who postulated that the sum of all forces equals zero for dynamic equilibrium of a mechanical system.

Thus for a multi-loop dynamic system (n degrees of freedom) we have at the rth mechanical node

$$\sum_{j=1}^{m} f_{r_j}(t) = 0 \quad \text{for } n \text{ nodes} \tag{4.16}$$

where $f_{r_j}(t)$ is the jth force at the rth node and a node is defined as the junction of one or more discrete elements.

Circuital Postulate

We have also the continuity of space postulate,[7] i.e. around any mechanical loop (say the rth loop) the summation of all displacements or velocities, taking account of sign, is zero.

Thus
$$\sum_{j=1}^{m} \omega_{r_j}(t) = 0 \quad \text{for } n \text{ loops} \tag{4.17}$$

where ω_{r_j} is the jth velocity in the rth loop of an n-loop system, and a loop is defined as a closed connection of discrete elements and energy sources. *Note:* The circuital postulate is the dual of the nodal postulate.

(b) *Electrical Systems*

Similarly in the electrical system we have Kirchhoff's two postulates:

Nodal Postulate

Summation of all currents, taking due account of signs, into a node is zero,

i.e.
$$\sum_{j=1}^{m} i_{r_j}(t) = 0 \quad \text{for } n \text{ nodes} \tag{4.18}$$

where $i_{r_j}(t)$ is the jth current flowing into the rth node of an n-node system.

Circuital Postulate

Summation of all voltages, taking due account of signs, around a loop is zero,

i.e. $$\sum_{j=1}^{m} e_{r_j}(t) = 0 \quad \text{for } n \text{ loops} \tag{4.19}$$

where $e_{r_j}(t)$ is the jth voltage in the rth loop of an n-loop system.

(c) Generalized Systems

We may generalize the nodal and circuital postulates as follows:

Nodal Postulate

Summation of all flow variables, taking due account of signs, into a node is zero,

i.e. $$\sum_{j=1}^{m} \beta_{r_j}(t) = 0 \quad \text{for } n \text{ nodes} \tag{4.20}$$

where $\beta_{r_j}(t)$ is the jth flow variable flowing into the rth node of an n-node system.

Circuital Postulate

Summation of all potential variables, taking due account of signs, around a loop is zero,

i.e. $$\sum_{j=1}^{m} \alpha_{r_j}(t) = 0 \quad \text{for } n \text{ loops} \tag{4.21}$$

where α_{r_j} is the jth potential variable in the rth loop of an n-loop system.

4.9 CONSTRUCTION OF ANALOGOUS NETWORKS

To construct a linear network which is analogous to another linear network we replace each potential variable in the latter with the potential variable in the analogous system. The flow variables are treated in a similar manner. Each energy storage element, energy dissipation element and energy transfer or gyration element in one system is replaced by its corresponding counterpart in the analogous system. The correspondence between variables and parameters for electrical and mechanical systems is given in Table 4.2.

For discrete parameter networks, discrete variable values may only be established at the end point of the bi-lateral elements. A bi-lateral element is defined as one in which the flow variable may be directed towards either end point or terminal. Discrete non-zero velocities, therefore, can only exist at individual masses (inertias) or at the junctions of two or more elements. These points in the system, as already stated, are called nodes.

To illustrate the detailed steps involved we will now consider the simplified model of a car suspension system which is shown in Fig. 4.7.[14]

Referring to Fig. 4.7(a)

M_{01} represents one-quarter of the mass of the car

M_{02} represents the mass of one wheel and effective mass of the axle

k_{02} represents the spring constant of the tyre

k_{12} represents the spring constant of the spring suspension

a_{12} represents the viscous friction coefficient of the damper

ω_1 represents the rectilinear vertical velocity of mass M_{01}

ω_2 represents the rectilinear vertical velocity of mass M_{02}

ω_0 represents the rectilinear vertical velocity of the tyre due to the forward velocity.

As shown in Fig. 4.7(b) there are three nodes where node 0 is ground, node 1 exists at the junction of a_{12}, k_{12} with mass M_{01} and node 2 exists at the junction of M_{02} with the remainder of the elements. Each parameter

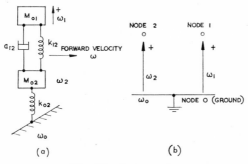

(a)   (b)

Fig. 4.7 *System nodes*

(a) *Car suspension system*   (b) *Nodes of system*

is designated subscripts which correspond to the nodes at the end points. One of the subscripts of each mass will always be 0 since the potential variable (velocity or displacement) is always measured with respect to ground reference (node 0). Thus the mass of the wheel axle is designated M_{02} since node 2 exists at the junction of this mass with the other elements.

Similarly the spring stiffness of the tyre having end points at nodes 0 and 2 is designated k_{02}.

A velocity is subscribed to each node as shown in Fig. 4.7(b).

With these conventions[15] the mechanical network may now be drawn as Fig. 4.8(a). The analogous electrical network is obtained by replacing each mechanical element by the corresponding electrical element as shown in Fig. 4.8(b). The nodes in the two systems must obviously be the same.

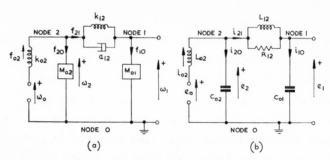

Fig. 4.8 *Equivalent networks of Fig. 4.7(a)*

(a) *Equivalent mechanical network*   (b) *Analogous electrical network*

If the nodal postulate is applied to each node in the two networks, the following equations are derived.

(a) *Mechanical network*

Node 1

$$f_{21} - f_{10} = 0$$

i.e.
$$a_{12}(\omega_2 - \omega_1) + k_{12}\int_{-\infty}^{t}(\omega_2 - \omega_1)\,dt - M_{01}\frac{d\omega_1}{dt} = 0 \qquad (4.22)$$

Node 2

$$f_{02} - f_{20} - f_{21} = 0$$

i.e.
$$k_{02}\int_{-\infty}^{t}(\omega_0 - \omega_2)\,dt - M_{02}\frac{d\omega_2}{dt} - a_{12}(\omega_2 - \omega_1)$$

$$-k_{12}\int_{-\infty}^{t}(\omega_2 - \omega_1)\,dt = 0 \qquad (4.23)$$

(b) *Electrical network*

Node 1

$$i_{21} - i_{10} = 0$$

i.e.
$$\frac{1}{R_{12}}(e_2 - e_1) + \frac{1}{L_{12}}\int_{-\infty}^{t}(e_2 - e_1)\,dt - C_{01}\frac{de_1}{dt} = 0 \qquad (4.24)$$

Node 2

$$i_{02} - i_{20} - i_{21} = 0$$

i.e. $\quad \dfrac{1}{L_{02}} \displaystyle\int_{-\infty}^{t} (e_0 - e_2)\, dt - C_{02} \dfrac{de_2}{dt} - \dfrac{1}{R_{12}} (e_2 - e_1)$

$$-\dfrac{1}{L_{12}} \int_{-\infty}^{t} (e_2 - e_1)\, dt = 0 \qquad (4.25)$$

The similarity is illustrated between the corresponding differential equations in respect of parameters and variables.

4.10 THE DUAL ANALOGOUS NETWORK

The dual analogous network corresponding to the direct analogous network of Fig. 4.8(b) may be constructed by applying the Principle of Duality.

Referring to Table 4.6 the nodal equation (4.24) for node 1 of the analogous network becomes the circuital equation for loop 1 of the dual network:

i.e. for loop 1 $\qquad e_{21} - e_{10} = 0$

and $\qquad R_{12}(i_2 - i_1) + \dfrac{1}{C_{12}} \displaystyle\int_{-\infty}^{t} (i_2 - i_1)\, dt - L_{01} \dfrac{di_1}{dt} = 0 \qquad (4.26)$

Similarly the nodal equation for node 2 of the analogous network becomes the circuital equation of loop 2 of the dual network, i.e.

$$e_{02} - e_{20} - e_{21} = 0$$

and $\qquad \dfrac{1}{C_{02}} \displaystyle\int_{-\infty}^{t} (i_0 - i_2)\, dt - L_{02} \dfrac{di_2}{dt} - R_{12}(i_2 - i_1)$

$$-\dfrac{1}{C_{12}} \int_{-\infty}^{t} (i_2 - i_1)\, dt = 0 \qquad (4.27)$$

The dual analogous network shown in Fig. 4.9 is constructed from a knowledge of these equations or alternatively from the direct dualization of the network of Fig. 4.8(b).

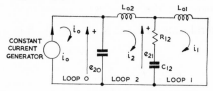

Fig. 4.9 *Dual analogous network of Fig. 4.7(a)*

Comparing equations (4.26) and (4.27) with equations (4.22) and (4.23) respectively we observe that the relationships shown in Table 4.7 are valid.

TABLE 4.7

Quantity	Dual-Analogous Quantity
Force	Voltage
Velocity	Current
Mass	Inductance
Spring Compliance	Capacitance
Viscous Friction Coefficient	Resistance

Although the dual analogous network of Fig. 4.9 is not easily identified with the mechanical network of Fig. 4.8 (b), it may, in certain applications be better to use such a network in preference to the direct analogous network.

The approach is valid for planar networks (i.e. those whose network branches may be drawn on the surface of a sphere) but it is not valid for non-planar networks since such a network has no dual.

In the actual construction of analogous networks, amplitude and time scale factors are incorporated and these are based on the three fundamental units: length, mass and time. This aspect will now be discussed.

4.11 SCALE FACTORS

The dimensions of all quantities involved in the dynamics of mechanical systems may be expressed in terms of the three fundamental units, i.e. mass 'M', length 'L' and time 't'. With mass, length and time relationships established, all other quantities are automatically determined.

(a) *Basic Scale Factors—Direct Analogy*

If we denote a general scale factor as S, we have the following relationships:

$$C = S_1 M$$
$$\int e(t_E)\,dt_E = \Psi(t_E) = S_2 L \qquad (4.28)$$
$$t_E = S_3 t_M$$

where C is capacitance, $\Psi(t)$ represents flux linkage, t_E is time in the electrical system and t_M is time in the mechanical system.

S_1, S_2 and S_3 represent the fundamental scale factors from which all other scale factors may be derived.

Note: A scale factor will be expressed in the units of one mechanical quantity divided by the units of the corresponding electrical quantity.

(b) Derived Scale Factors

These are determined by expressing all quantities involved in a relationship in terms of M, L and t.

(i) Current–Force—Scale Factor S_4

$$i(t_E) = S_4 f(t_M) = C\frac{de(t_E)}{dt_E}$$

$$= S_4 M L t_M^{-2} = S_1 M \frac{S_2 L}{t_E^2}$$

$$= S_1 M \frac{S_2 L}{S_3^2 t_M^2}$$

$$\text{i.e.} \quad S_4 = \frac{S_1 S_2}{S_3^2} \tag{4.29}$$

(ii) Voltage–Velocity—Scale Factor S_5

$$e(t_E) = S_5 \omega(t_M) = S_5 L t_M^{-1}$$

$$\frac{d}{dt_E}\Psi(t_E) = \frac{S_2 L t_M^{-1}}{S_3}$$

i.e.
$$S_5 = \frac{S_2}{S_3} \tag{4.30}$$

(iii) Inductance–Spring Compliance—Scale Factor S_6

$$L = \frac{S_6}{k} = \frac{S_6 L}{L M t_M^{-2}}$$

$$= \frac{\int e(t_E)\,dt_E}{i(t_E)} = \frac{S_2 L}{S_1 S_2 L M S_3^{-2} t_M^{-2}}$$

i.e.
$$S_6 = \frac{S_3^2}{S_1} \tag{4.31}$$

(iv) *Resistance–Reciprocal of Viscous Friction Coefficient — Scale Factor S_7*

$$R = \frac{S_7}{a} = \frac{S_7 \, L t_M^{-1}}{L M t_M^{-2}} = \frac{S_7}{M t_M^{-1}}$$

$$= \frac{e(t_E)}{i(t_E)} = \frac{S_2 \, S_3^{-1} \, L \, t_M^{-1}}{S_1 \, S_2 \, L M S_3^{-2} \, t_M^{-2}} = \frac{S_3}{S_1 \, M t_M^{-1}}$$

i.e. $$S_7 = \frac{S_3}{S_1} \qquad\qquad (4.32)$$

Application to Car Suspension Problem

Let us apply these scale factors to the car suspension problem given that, in a consistent set of units

$$M_{01} = 20 \quad M_{02} = 1 \quad k_{12} = 500 \quad k_{02} = 4000 \quad a_{12} = 100 \quad \text{and} \quad \omega_0 = 1$$

Typically in engineer's units we would have

Mass expressed in slugs, k in pound-force/foot,
a in pound-force/foot per second and ω_0 in feet per second

With these values we may select three and only three independent scale factors. These need not necessarily be the three basic scale factors, as it may be preferable to select one or more of the desired scale factors so that suitable values of analogous elements are given.

Typically we might choose S_1 to be 10^{-8} farad per slug giving a maximum capacitance value of 0.2 microfarad. If we also wish to restrict the maximum value of inductance to say 0.2 henry, we choose S_6 to be 100 henries/unit spring compliance

i.e. $$S_6 = 100$$

Finally to ensure suitable voltage levels we may choose $S_5 = 100$ volts/foot per second to give a maximum excitation voltage of 100 volts. We have now chosen scale factors S_1, S_5 and S_6. From the latter, all other scale factors must be derived.

Thus $$S_3^2 = S_1 \, S_6 = 10^{-8} \times 10^2 \quad \text{[from equation (4.31)]}$$

i.e. $$S_3 = 10^{-3}$$

S_3 expresses the relationship between the time sequence of events in the electrical system and those in the mechanical system. With $S = 10^{-3}$, the time variation of variables in the analogous electrical system is one thousand times faster than the time variation of variables in the mechanical system.

$$S_2 = S_3 S_5 \qquad \text{[from equation (4.30)]}$$

$$= 10^{-3} \times 10^2 = 10^{-1} \text{ flux linkage per foot}$$

and
$$S_4 = \frac{S_1 S_2}{S_3^2} \qquad \text{[from equation (4.29)]}$$

$$= 10^{-8} \times 10^{-1} \times 10^6 = 10^{-3} \text{ ampere/pound-force}$$

Finally
$$S_7 = \frac{S_3}{S_1} \qquad \text{[from equation (4.32)]}$$

$$= 10^{-3} \times 10^8 = 10^5 \text{ ohms per} \left(\frac{\text{feet per second}}{\text{pound-force}}\right)$$

With these scale factors,

$$C_{01} = S_1 M_{01} = 10^{-8} \times 20 = 0{\cdot}2 \times 10^{-6} \text{ farad}$$

$$C_{02} = S_1 M_{02} = 10^{-8} \times 1 \;\;= 0{\cdot}01 \times 10^{-6} \text{ farad}$$

$$L_{02} = \frac{S_6}{k_{02}} \;\;= \frac{10^2}{4 \times 10^3} \;\;= 0{\cdot}025 \text{ henry}$$

$$L_{12} = \frac{S_6}{k_{12}} \;\;= \frac{10^2}{5 \times 10^2} \;\;= 0{\cdot}2 \text{ henry}$$

$$R_{12} = \frac{S_7}{a_{12}} \;\;= \frac{10^5}{10^2} \;\;= 10^3 \text{ ohm}$$

$$e_0(t_E) = \;\;\;\;\; S_5 \,\omega_0(t_M) \;\;\;\;\; = 100 \text{ volt}$$

The analogous electrical networks with these values incorporated is shown in Fig. 4.10.

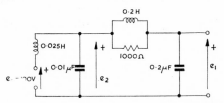

Fig. 4.10 *Scaled analogous network of Fig.* 4.7 (a)

With such a network the response of the system to varying road conditions would be investigated by choosing e_0 to be a time varying voltage corresponding to the time variation of road surface elevation.

The derivation of scale factors for the dual analogous network may be derive in a similar manner.

4.12 NETWORK ELEMENT TRANSFORMS

The integro-differential equations which describe the dynamic performance of linear networks may be solved by the use of the one-sided Laplace transformation.[16] The latter is a functional transformation and it transforms a certain class of functions of a real variable into functions of a complex variable 's'. Thus a linear integro-differential equation with a real independent time variable 't' is transformed into a linear algebraic equation in the complex variable s, where $s \triangleq \sigma + j\omega$, σ and ω are real numbers and $j^2 \triangleq -1$.

If a function of time $f(t)$ has a Laplace Transform $F(s)$ we write

$$f(t) \supset F(s) \tag{4.33}$$

The inverse relationship is expressed as

$$F(s) \subset f(t) \tag{4.34}$$

Thus the solution of the transformed equations as functions of s, when transformed back to the time-domain, represents the solution of the original integro-differential equations

$$F(s) \triangleq s \int_0^\infty f(t) e^{-st} \, dt \tag{4.35}$$

with the restriction that $f(t)$ must satisfy the Dirichlet conditions, i.e. it must be a single valued function, have a finite number of maxima and minima and a finite number of finite discontinuities.

In addition $\int_0^\infty e^{-ct} |f(t)| \, dt$ must exist where c is a real number.

The inverse relationship from the s-domain to the time-domain is expressed as

$$f(t) = \frac{1}{2\pi j} \int_{c-j\infty}^{c+j\infty} e^{st} \frac{F(s)}{s} \, ds \tag{4.36}$$

where real part of s (i.e. σ) $> c$.

Equations (4.35) and (4.36) constitute the Fourier-Mellin pair.

Note: Attention is restricted to the positive time-domain $0 \leq t \leq \infty$.

Tables of transform pairs $f(t)$ and $F(s)$ may be constructed for standard types of functions and a selection of these, together with some simple applications of transform methods, are given in Appendix A.1.

However, in the analysis of linear, discrete-parameter, time-invariant networks, by the Laplace transform method, it is not necessary to construct the integro-differential equations if the network element parameters are transformed directly. This procedure is valid since the generalized nodal and circuital postulates also apply in the s-domain.

To illustrate this point consider equations (4.24) and (4.25)

i.e.
$$\frac{1}{R_{12}}(e_2-e_1)+\frac{1}{L_{12}}\int_{-\infty}^{t}(e_2-e_1)\,dt-C_{01}\frac{de_1}{dt}=0$$

and
$$\frac{1}{L_{02}}\int_{-\infty}^{t}(e_0-e_2)\,d\ -C_{02}\frac{de_2}{dt}-\frac{1}{R_{12}}(e_2-e_1)-\frac{1}{L_{12}}\int_{-\infty}^{t}(e_2-e_1)\,dt=0$$

If we are interested only in the solution of the equations in the range $0<t<\infty$, these equations are modified by multiplying each term by unit step function $\mu_0(t)$. As shown in Section 4.3.2 the equations may be expressed in the form

$$\frac{1}{R_{12}}(e_2-e_1)\mu_0(t)+\frac{1}{L_{12}}\int_{0}^{t}(e_2-e_1)\mu_0(t)\,dt+i_{12}(0)\mu_0(t)$$

$$-C_{01}\left\{\frac{d}{dt}[e_1\mu_0(t)]-e_1(0)\mu_1(t)\right\}=0$$

$$\frac{1}{L_{02}}\int_{0}^{t}(e_2-e_1)\mu_0(t)\,dt+i_{02}(0)\mu_0(t)-C_{02}\left\{\frac{d}{dt}[e_2\mu_0(t)]-e_2(0)\mu_1(t)\right\}$$

$$-\frac{1}{R_{12}}(e_2-e_1)\mu_0(t)-\frac{1}{L_{12}}\int_{0}^{t}(e_2-e_1)\mu_0(t)\,dt-i_{12}(0)\mu_0(t)=0\quad(4.37)$$

where $\mu_1(t)$ represents unit impulse function as defined in Appendix A.1, and $i_{01}(0)$, $i_{02}(0)$ and $i_{12}(0)$ represent the respective current values at $t=0$.

These equations may now be transformed (see Appendix A.1) giving the result

$$\frac{1}{R_{12}}[E_2(s)-E_1(s)]+\frac{1}{sL_{12}}[E_2(s)-E_1(s)]$$

$$+i_{21}(0^+)-sC_{01}[E_1(s)-e_1(0^+)]=0$$

$$\frac{1}{sL_{02}}[E_2(s)-E_1(s)]+i_{02}(0^+)-sC_{02}[E_2(s)-e_2(0^+)]$$

$$-\frac{1}{R_{12}}[E_2(s)-E_1(s)]-\frac{1}{sL_{12}}[E_2(s)-E_1(s)]-i_{21}(0^+)=0\quad(4.38)$$

where (0^+) means the value of the variable at $t = 0^+$, which is defined as the limiting value of t as t approaches the origin along the positive time axis.

The network elements of Fig. 4.8 (b) may be represented as shown in Fig. 4.11.

These network element transforms have been derived from the original integro-differential equations. It is obvious that the network element transforms could be used directly in the construction of Fig. 4.11.

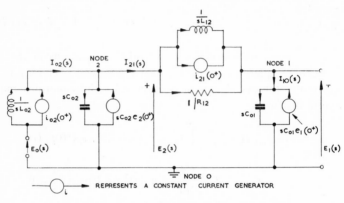

Fig. 4.11 *Network element transforms of Fig.* 4.8

We observe that an inductance L when transformed, on a nodal basis, becomes $1/sL$ connected in parallel with a constant current generator, representing the initial current flowing through the inductor at $t = 0^+$, and in the same direction as the current flowing through the inductor after $t = 0$. We also observe that a capacitance C when transformed, on a nodal basis, becomes sC connected in parallel with a constant current generator representing the initial current flowing at $t = 0^+$ and in a direction opposed to that of the current flowing through the capacitor after $t = 0$.

The dissipator element, i.e. resistance R, has no energy storage and therefore when transformed is not a function of s nor has it any initial condition.

These concepts may be expressed in terms of the generalized variables $\alpha(t)$ and $\beta(t)$ and these are given in Table 4.8 when transforms are carried out on a nodal basis and on a circuital basis.

On a nodal basis the transformed quantities such as $1/sL$ and sC, or in generalized form $1/s\lambda_L$ and $s\lambda_c$ are called admittance functions with the general notation $Y(s)$.

TABLE 4.8—GENERALIZED LINEAR NETWORK ELEMENT TRANSFORMS*

Time-Domain Representation	s-Domain Representation

(i) Energy dissipation element λ_R where $\lambda_R = \dfrac{\alpha(t)}{\beta(t)}$ and $\lambda_G = \dfrac{1}{\lambda_R}$

Circuital

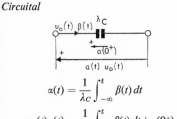

$$\alpha(t) = \lambda_R \beta(t)$$

Circuital

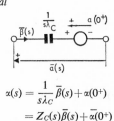

$$\bar\alpha(s) = \lambda_R \bar\beta(s)$$

Nodal

$$\beta(t) = \lambda_G \alpha(t)$$

Nodal

$$\bar\beta(s) = \lambda_G \bar\alpha(s)$$

(ii) Energy storage element λ_C where $\lambda_C = \dfrac{1}{\alpha(t)} \int \beta(t)\, dt$

Circuital

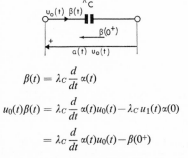

$$\alpha(t) = \frac{1}{\lambda_C} \int_{-\infty}^{t} \beta(t)\, dt$$

$$u_0(t)\alpha(t) = \frac{1}{\lambda_C} \int_{0^+}^{t} \beta(t)\, dt + \alpha(0^+)$$

Circuital

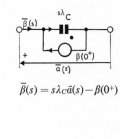

$$\alpha(s) = \frac{1}{s\lambda_C} \bar\beta(s) + \alpha(0^+)$$

$$= Z_C(s)\bar\beta(s) + \bar\alpha(0^+)$$

Nodal

$$\beta(t) = \lambda_C \frac{d}{dt} \alpha(t)$$

$$u_0(t)\beta(t) = \lambda_C \frac{d}{dt} \alpha(t)u_0(t) - \lambda_C u_1(t)\alpha(0)$$

$$= \lambda_C \frac{d}{dt} \alpha(t)u_0(t) - \beta(0^+)$$

Nodal

$$\bar\beta(s) = s\lambda_C \bar\alpha(s) - \beta(0^+)$$

* This table is a generalized form of a table for electric network elements proposed by S. R. Deards, College of Aeronautics, Cranfield, as an unpublished lecture supplement.

TABLE 4.8—*Continued*

Time-Domain Representation	*s-Domain Representation*

(iii) Energy storage element λ_L where $\lambda_L = \dfrac{1}{\beta(t)} \displaystyle\int \alpha(t)\, dt$

Circuital	*Circuital*

$$\alpha(t) = \lambda_L \frac{d}{dt}\beta(t)$$

$$u_0(t)\alpha(t) = \lambda_L \frac{d}{dt}\beta(t)u_0(t) - \lambda_L \beta(0)u_1(t)$$

$$= \lambda_L \frac{d}{dt}\beta(t)u_0(t) - \alpha(0^+)$$

$$\bar{\alpha}(s) = Z_L(s)\bar{\beta}(s) - \alpha(0^+)$$

$$= s\lambda_L(s)\beta(s) - \alpha(0^+)$$

Nodal	*Nodal*

$$\beta(t) = \frac{1}{\lambda_L}\int_{-\infty}^{t} \alpha(t)\, dt$$

$$u_0(t)\beta(t) = \frac{1}{\lambda_L}\int_{0^+}^{t} \alpha(t)\, dt + \frac{1}{\lambda_L}\int_{-\infty}^{0} a(t)\, dt$$

$$= \frac{1}{\lambda_L}\int_{0^+}^{t} \alpha(t)\, dt + \beta(0^+)$$

$$\bar{\beta}(s) = \frac{1}{s\lambda_L}\bar{\alpha}(s) + \beta(0^+)$$

$$= Y_L(s)\bar{\alpha}(s) + \beta(0^+)$$

$Y(s)$ is defined as $\dfrac{\text{Laplace Transform of Flow Variable}}{\text{Laplace Transform of Potential Variable}}$, with zero initial conditions.

On a circuital basis, the transformed quantities such as sL and $1/sC$ or in generalized form $s\lambda_L$ and $1/s\lambda_c$ are called impedance functions with the general notation $Z(s)$.

We have $Z(s) \triangleq \dfrac{1}{Y}(s) = \dfrac{\text{Laplace Transform of Potential Variable}}{\text{Laplace Transform of Flow Variable}}$, with zero initial conditions.

Thus for electrical systems

$$Y(s) = \frac{1}{Z(s)} = \frac{I(s)}{E(s)}$$

and for mechanical systems

$$Y(s) = \frac{1}{Z(s)} = \frac{F(s)}{\bar{\omega}(s)}$$

(4.39)

where $F(s)$ represents the Laplace Transform of force $f(t)$ and $\bar{\omega}(s)$ represents the Laplace Transform of linear velocity.

4.13 SYSTEMS WITH COMBINED TRANSLATION AND ROTATION

In Section 4.9 we considered the construction of the analogous electrical network of a mechanical system having rectilinear motion. Rotational systems may be treated in a similar manner by using the correct corresponding analogous quantities as given in Table 4.2.

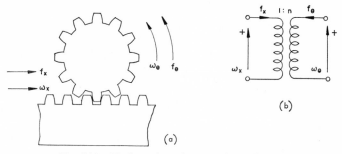

Fig. 4.12 *Ideal rectilinear/rotational transformer*
(a) *Rack and pinion unit*   (b) *Network representation*

In dealing with linear, discrete-element systems there is a requirement for a special form of ideal transformer in which an angular velocity potential at one pair of terminals is transformed to a linear velocity potential at the other pair of terminals and vice-versa. In other words the ideal transformer, in the form of ideal gears, for rotational systems is replaced by, say, the ideal rack and pinion unit as shown in Fig. 4.12.

For the ideal element giving transfer of energy without loss we have

$$\omega_\theta(t) = n\omega_x(t)$$

$$f_x(t) = -nf_\theta(t)$$

(4.40)

where n represents the transfer ratio.

If now we specify n_1 teeth for the rotational gear and n_2 teeth per unit length for the rectilinear gear, then

$$n = \frac{2\pi n_2}{n_1} \tag{4.41}$$

Now since n_2 has unit of length^{-1}, n also has units of length^{-1}.

The translational gear may be regarded as a rotary gear with infinite radius and thus is a special case of the latter.

Example of Coupled Translation and Rotation

The example shown in Fig. 4.13 is taken from page 289 of Reference 5. It illustrates a machine mounted so that the transmission of force f_{0x} to the supporting structure is reduced to a minimum. The machine is subject

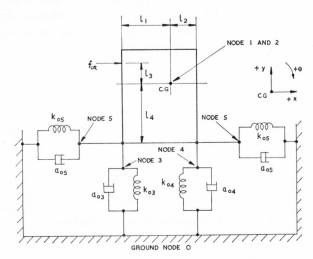

Fig. 4.13 *Three degrees of freedom suspension*

to translation along x and y directions, rotation θ in the xy plane and therefore the system has three degrees of freedom.

The block representing the machine is characterized by a mass M in the x and y degrees of freedom and a polar moment of inertia J in the θ degrees of freedom.

We may therefore redraw Fig. 4.13 as shown in Fig. 4.14 where ideal elements are represented including infinite stiffness linkages.

The coupling between the x and y degrees of freedom is due to the angular motion in the θ degree of freedom.

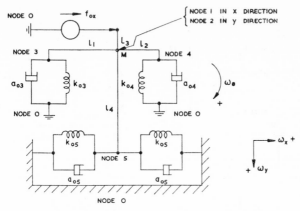

Fig. 4.14 *Equivalent link diagram of Fig. 4.13*

ω_θ *represents angular velocity* ω_x *represents velocity in X direction*
ω_y *represents velocity in Y direction*

Referring to Fig. 4.14, we observe that the force $f_{0x}(t)$, acting at a distance l_3 from the centre of gravity C.G., results in a torque $l_3 f_{0x}(t)$ acting on the polar moment of inertia J at, say, node 6 and a force $f_{0x}(t)$ acting on the mass M at node 1 in the x direction.

The body also has mass M in the y direction and this is designated as node 2.

The angular motion in the θ degree of freedom is coupled to the x and y degrees of freedom, respectively, by means of ideal transformers of the form discussed at the beginning of this section.

The transformers are illustrated in Fig. 4.15.

The complete network may now be constructed by connecting to the nodes the relevant elements, in addition to the flow variable $f_{0x}(t)$ flowing between node 0 and 1.

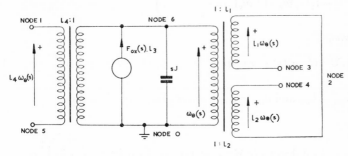

Fig. 4.15 *Equivalent network for 'θ' degree of freedom*

115

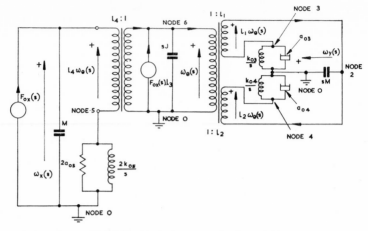

Fig. 4.16 *Equivalent network of Fig.* 4.14

The complete network is shown in Fig. 4.16 (assuming zero initial conditions).

Applying the Nodal Postulate to node 1

$$F_{0x}(s) - \omega_x(s)sM - \left[(\omega_x(s) - l_4\omega_\theta(s))\left(2a_{05} + \frac{2k_{05}}{s}\right)\right] = 0$$

For Node 6

$$F_{0x}(s)l_3 - sJ\omega_\theta(s) + l_4\left[(\omega_x(s) - l_4\omega_\theta(s))\left(2a_{05} + \frac{2k_{05}}{s}\right)\right]$$

$$-l_2(l_2\omega_\theta(s) - \omega_y(s))\left(\frac{k_{04}}{s} + a_{04}\right)$$

$$-l_1(l_1\omega_\theta(s) + \omega_y(s))\left(\frac{k_{03}}{s} + a_{03}\right) = 0$$

For Node 2

$$\omega_y(s)sM + (l_1\omega_\theta(s) + \omega_y(s))\left(\frac{k_{04}}{s} + a_{04}\right) - (l_2\omega_\theta(s) - \omega_y(s))\left(\frac{k_{03}}{s} + a_{03}\right) = 0$$

For $k_{03} = k_{04}$ and $a_{03} = a_{04}$ the nodal equations become

Node 1

$$F_{0x}(s) - \omega_x(s)sM - \left[(\omega_x(s) - l_4\omega_\theta(s))\left(2a_{05} + \frac{2k_{05}}{s}\right)\right] = 0$$

Node 6

$$F_{0x}(s)l_3 - sJ\omega_\theta(s) + l_4\left[(\omega_x(s) - l_4\,\omega_\theta(s))\left(2a_{05} + \frac{2k_{05}}{s}\right)\right]$$

$$- \left[\omega_\theta(s)(l_1^2 + l_2^2) + \omega_y(s)(l_1 - l_2)\right]\left[\frac{k_{03}}{s} + a_{03}\right] = 0$$

Node 2

$$\omega_y(s)sM + \left[\omega_\theta(s)(l_1 - l_2) + 2\omega_y(s)\right]\left[\frac{k_{03}}{s} + a_{03}\right] = 0$$

The analogous electrical network corresponding to Fig. 4.16 is obtained directly, as before, by replacing each mechanical element by its corresponding analogous electrical element.

Scale factors would have to be incorporated in the manner already discussed. In such applications the need for ideal transformers presents some difficulty and the network may be reduced to obviate the need for these. However, if this procedure is carried out there is no longer a direct correspondence between elements of this reduced electrical network and the original mechanical network.

4.14 ELECTROMECHANICAL NETWORKS

4.14.1 The Basic D.C. Electromechanical Transducer

The purpose of any electromechanical transducer is to convert electrical energy to mechanical energy or vice-versa. The coupling may be magnetic or electric and in the most general form of transducer there may be n electrical ports and m mechanical ports.

We shall confine our attention, for the sake of simplicity, to the response of the mechanical variables at one mechanical port to the excitation at one electrical port. The reciprocal case may be carried out in a similar manner.

Electromagnetic Coupling

(i) *Rectilinear Motion*

If current i and co-ordinate x are the independent variables then

$$\text{force } f_x = -\frac{\partial}{\partial x}W_m + i\frac{\partial\phi}{\partial x} \tag{4.42}$$

where W_m is the stored energy in the magnetic field and ϕ is the flux linkage.

$$W_m = \tfrac{1}{2}\int_{\text{volume}} BH \; v \tag{4.43}$$

117

where B is the flux density, H is the magnetic force and v is the volume of the field.

$$e = \frac{d}{dt}\phi(i, x)$$

$$= \frac{\partial\phi(i, x)}{\partial i}\frac{di}{dt} + \frac{\partial\phi(i, x)}{\partial x}\frac{dx}{dt} \qquad (4.44)$$

where e is the electromotive force.

(ii) *Angular Motion*

If current i and co-ordinate θ are the independent variables

$$f_\theta = -\frac{\partial W_m}{\partial\theta} + i\frac{\partial\phi}{\partial\theta}$$

$$e = \frac{d}{dt}\phi(i, \theta)$$

$$= \frac{\partial}{\partial i}\phi(i, \theta)\frac{di}{dt} + \frac{\partial}{\partial\theta}\phi(i, \theta)\frac{d\theta}{dt} \qquad (4.46)$$

where f_θ is the torque.

Electric Field Coupling

(i) *Rectilinear Motion*

If voltage e and co-ordinate x are the independent variables

$$f_x = -\frac{\partial}{\partial x}W_e + e\frac{\partial q}{\partial x} \qquad (4.47)$$

where W_e is the energy stored in the electric field, q is total charge and f_x is force

$$W_e = \tfrac{1}{2}\int_{volume} DE\, dv \qquad (4.48)$$

where D is the electric flux density, E is the electric field force, and v is the volume of the field.

$$i(t) = \frac{d}{dt}q(e, x)$$

$$= \frac{\partial q}{\partial e}(e, x)\frac{de}{dt} + \frac{\partial q}{\partial x}(e, x)\frac{dx}{dt} \qquad (4.49)$$

(ii) *Angular Motion*

If voltage e and co-ordinate θ are the independent variables

$$f_\theta = -\frac{\partial W_e}{\partial \theta} + e\frac{\partial q}{\partial \theta} \tag{4.50}$$

$$i = \frac{\partial q(e, \theta)}{\partial e}\frac{de}{dt} + \frac{\partial q(e, \theta)}{\partial \theta}\frac{d\theta}{dt} \tag{4.51}$$

4.14.2   Two-Port Network Representations[17]

For these representations to be valid, certain assumptions regarding parameters have to be imposed. In other words the assumptions must be such that there is a linear relationship between the mechanical variables and the electrical variables.

Magnetic Coupling

As an example of these constraints consider the case of rectilinear motion.

Let us impose constraints as follows:

$$\frac{\partial W_m}{\partial x} = 0$$

$$\frac{\partial \phi}{\partial x} = k_m \text{ (constant)} \tag{4.52}$$

$$\frac{\partial \phi}{\partial i} = 0$$

From equation (4.42) $\qquad f_x = i\frac{\partial \phi}{\partial x} = k_m i$

$$\tag{4.53}$$

From equation (4.44) $\qquad e = \frac{\partial \phi}{\partial x}\frac{dx}{dt} = k_m \omega_x$

where $\qquad \omega_x(t) = \frac{dx}{dt}$

Thus in matrix notation

$$\begin{bmatrix} e \\ i \end{bmatrix} = \begin{bmatrix} k_m & 0 \\ 0 & \dfrac{1}{k_m} \end{bmatrix}\begin{bmatrix} \omega_x \\ f_x \end{bmatrix} \tag{4.54}$$

Two-port network representation is shown in Fig. 4.17.

Fig. 4.17 *Electromechanical transducer*

Electric Field Coupling

Consider again rectilinear motion with imposed constraints

$$\frac{\partial W_e}{\partial x} = 0$$

$$\frac{\partial q}{\partial x} = k_e \text{ (constant)} \qquad (4.55)$$

$$\frac{\partial q}{\partial e} = 0$$

Thus

$$f_x = e\frac{\partial q}{\partial x} = k_e e$$

$$i = \frac{\partial q}{\partial x}\frac{dx}{dt} = k_e \omega_x \qquad (4.56)$$

Thus

$$\begin{bmatrix} e \\ i \end{bmatrix} = \begin{bmatrix} 0 & \dfrac{1}{k_e} \\ k_e & 0 \end{bmatrix}\begin{bmatrix} \omega_x \\ f_x \end{bmatrix}$$

$$= \begin{bmatrix} 0 & 1 \\ 1 & 0 \end{bmatrix}\begin{bmatrix} k_e & 0 \\ 0 & \dfrac{1}{k_e} \end{bmatrix}\begin{bmatrix} \omega_x \\ f_x \end{bmatrix} \qquad (4.57)$$

Note: $\begin{bmatrix} 0 & 1 \\ 1 & 0 \end{bmatrix}$ represents the transmission matrix of a gyrator which is necessary in this case since electrostatic energy is converted to kinetic energy.

Thus we have the network configuration for the electric field transducer as shown in Fig. 4.18.

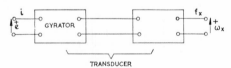

Fig. 4.18 *Electric field transducer*

4.14.3   Armature Controlled D.C. Motor

This is taken as a simple practical example of an electric magnetic transducer.

We assume that the field current is constant and thus independent of the armature current i_a.

We consider the motor to comprise a basic rotating armature transducer to which are connected electrical impedances at the input port and mechanical impedances at the output port.

The basic armature transducer is shown in Fig. 4.19.

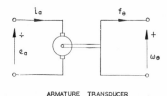

ARMATURE   TRANSDUCER

Fig. 4.19   *Basic rotating armature transducer*

From (4.45) assuming $\partial W_m/\partial\theta = 0$ (approximately valid for a practical machine) we have

$$f_\theta = i_a\frac{\partial\phi}{\partial\theta}(i_f,\theta) = K_m i_a \quad \text{(since } i_f \text{ is constant)}$$

$$e_a = \frac{d}{dt}\phi(i_f,\theta)$$

$$= \frac{\partial\phi}{\partial i}(i_f,\theta)\frac{di_f}{dt} + \frac{\partial}{\partial\theta}\phi(i_f,\theta)\frac{d\theta}{dt} \tag{4.58}$$

$$= K_m\omega_\theta \quad \text{(since } i_f \text{ is constant)}$$

where e_a is the armature voltage across brushes, i_a is the armature current, f_θ is the torque output, $\omega_\theta = d\theta/dt$ is the angular velocity of output shaft.

K_m is a constant in this case (i.e. mean value of $\partial\phi/\partial\theta$) which is dependent on the physical dimensions and number of poles of the machine.

If we now include the armature circuit impedance $Z_a(s)$ and mechanical load impedance $Z_m(s)$ we have the network configuration shown in Fig. 4.20.

From (4.58) we have

$$F_\theta(s) = K_m I_a(s)$$
$$E_a(s) = K_m \omega_\theta(s)$$

(4.59)

(assuming zero initial conditions).

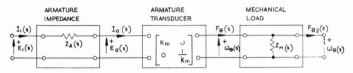

Fig. 4.20 *Basic arrangement for armature-controlled d.c. motor*

Typically $Z_a(s)$ will include resistance and linear incremental self inductance of the armature circuit

i.e.

$$Z_a(s) = R_a + sL_a$$

(4.60)

where R_a is armature circuit resistance, L_a is self inductance of armature.

A typical mechanical impedance would comprise the spring constant K of the shaft and load, viscous friction coefficient b of shaft and load in the bearings, and the polar moment of inertia J of shaft and load

i.e.

$$Y_m(s) = \frac{1}{Z_m(s)} = sJ + b + \frac{K}{s}$$

(4.61)

The network may, therefore, be drawn as in Fig. 4.21.

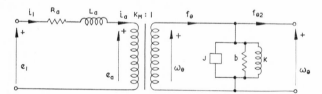

Fig. 4.21 *Network for armature-controlled d.c. motor*

The analogous electrical circuit may again be directly derived by replacing mechanical parameters and variables by their corresponding analogous electrical counterparts. Note that in this case the ideal transformer has a turns ratio of $1/K_m$ where K_m has the dimensions of volts per unit angular velocity. This fact must be borne in mind when incorporating scale factors. For further discussion on more detailed aspects of transducers, see Reference 17.

4.15 DIRECT SIMULATION ON THE ANALOGUE COMPUTER

The linear time-invariant, discrete parameter elements may be simulated directly on the analogue computer.

From Table 4.8 we have

(i) the generalized energy dissipation element λ_R

$$\text{where } \alpha(t) = \lambda_R \beta(t)$$

$$\beta(t) = \frac{1}{\lambda_R} \alpha(t)$$

(ii) the generalized energy storage element λ_c

$$\text{where } \alpha(t) = \frac{1}{\lambda_c} \int \beta(t)\, dt \tag{4.62}$$

(iii) the generalized storage element λ_L

$$\text{where } \beta(t) = \frac{1}{\lambda_L} \int \alpha(t)\, dt$$

Note: $\alpha(t)$ is the generalized potential variable and $\beta(t)$ is the generalized flow variable.

If we have the following computer variables

$$V_{\alpha,0} = a_{\alpha,0}\, \alpha(t)$$
$$V_{\beta,0} = a_{\beta,0}\, \beta(t) \tag{4.63}$$

where $a_{\alpha,0}$ and $a_{\beta,0}$ are amplitude scale factors.

Then for relation (i)

$$\alpha(t) = \lambda_R \beta(t)$$

$$V_{\alpha,0} = \frac{a_{\alpha,0}\, \lambda_R}{a_{\beta,0}}\, V_{\beta,0} = A V_{\beta,0} \tag{4.64}$$

If $A > 1$ we may use the configuration shown in Fig. 4.22 (a).
We must then take account of the sign reversal.
If $A \leq 1$ we may use a passive potentiometer unit as shown in Fig. 4.22 (b).

For relation (ii)

$$\alpha(t) = \frac{1}{\lambda_c} \int \beta(t)\, dt$$

$$V_{\alpha,0} = -\frac{a_{\alpha,0}}{\lambda_c\, a_{\beta,0}} \int -V_{\beta,0}\, dt \tag{4.65}$$

123

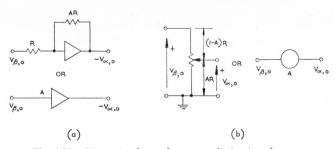

(a)   (b)

Fig. 4.22 *Direct simulators for energy dissipation elements*

(a) $A > 1$ (b) $A \leq 1$

Similarly for relation (iii)

$$V_{\beta,0} = -\frac{a_{\beta,0}}{\lambda_L a_{\alpha,0}} \int -V_{\alpha,0}\, dt \qquad (4.66)$$

The relationships expressed by equations (4.65) or (4.66) may be simulated on a conventional analogue integrator as shown in Fig. 4.23 where the sign reversal must again be taken into account. The application of this technique to discrete-parameter time-invariant systems is described in Reference 18, in which the direct simulators of each element are inter-connected in the same way as the original network. This procedure ensures that the number of integrators used in the simulator is the same as the number of storage elements in the system. Moreover, there is a direct correspondence between elements in the actual system and the analogous system, which is not the case if simulation is performed on the network nodal or circuital equations. Again in the simulation of the network

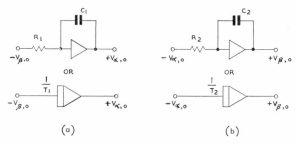

(a)   (b)

Fig. 4.23 *Direct simulators for energy storage elements*

(a) $T_1 = R_1 C_1 = \dfrac{\lambda_c a_{\beta,0}}{a_{\alpha,0}}$ (b) $T_2 = R_2 C_2 = \dfrac{\lambda_L a_{\alpha,0}}{a_{\beta,0}}$

$$V_{\alpha,0} = -\frac{1}{T_1} \int -V_{\beta,0}\, dt \qquad V_{\beta,0} = -\frac{1}{T_2} \int -V_{\alpha,0}\, dt$$

equations the number of integrators used may exceed the number of storage elements in the system. Another advantage of this direct simulation approach is that it can be extended to non-linear systems with the result that the non-linear network equations need not be derived.

As discussed in Reference 18 for a junction of three or more similar elements a modification is necessary to the direct interconnection of direct simulators.

As a simple example of this approach we will consider the simulation of network (b), Fig. 4.8, which, for convenience, is reproduced as part (a) of Fig. 4.24.

We have

$$i_{02} = \frac{1}{L_{02}} \int (e_0 - e_2) \, dt$$

$$e_2 = \frac{1}{C_{02}} \int i_{20} \, dt = \frac{1}{C_{02}} \int (i_{02} - i_{21}) \, dt$$

$$i_{21} = \frac{1}{L_{12}} \int (e_2 - e_1) \, dt + \frac{1}{R_{12}} (e_2 - e_1)$$

$$e_1 = \frac{1}{C_{01}} \int i_{10} \, dt = \frac{1}{C_{01}} \int i_{21} \, dt \qquad (4.67)$$

$$i_{21} = i_{10} = i_L - i_R$$

$$i_{02} - i_{21} = i_{20}$$

With the following amplitude scale factors we have the computing equations given in equation (4.68)

$$V_{e_0} = a_{e_0} e_0$$

$$V_{e_1} = a_{e_1} e_1$$

$$V_{e_2} = a_{e_2} e_2$$

$$V_{i_{02}} = a_{i_{02}} i_{02}$$

$$V_{i_{21}} = a_{i_{21}} i_{21} = a_{i_{21}} i_L + a_{i_{21}} i_R$$

$$V_{i_{20}} = a_{i_{20}} i_{20}$$

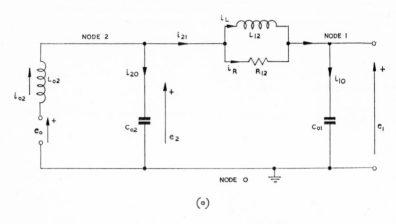

(a)

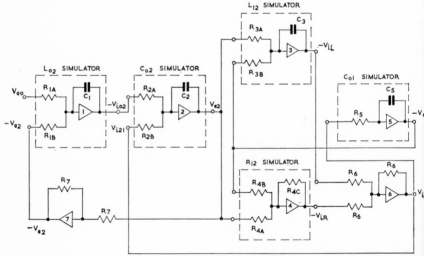

Fig. 4.24 *Simple example of direct simulation technique*

(a) *Network* (b) *of Fig.* 4.8   (b) *Direct simulation of above network*

Computing Equations

L_{02} *Simulator*

$$-V_{io2} = -\frac{1}{R_{1A}C_1}\int V_{eo}\,dt - \frac{1}{R_{1B}C_1}\int -V_{e2}\,dt$$

where

$$R_{1A}C_1 = \frac{a_{eo}L_{02}}{a_{io2}} \qquad R_{1B}C_1 = \frac{a_{e2}L_{02}}{a_{io2}}$$

C_{02} *Simulator*

$$V_{e2} = -\frac{1}{R_{2A}C_2}\int -V_{io2}\,dt - \frac{1}{R_{2B}C_2}\int V_{i21}\,dt$$

where

$$R_{2A}C_2 = \frac{a_{io2}C_{02}}{a_{e2}} \qquad R_{2B}C_2 = \frac{a_{i21}C_{02}}{a_{e2}}$$

L_{12} *Simulator*

$$-V_{iL} = -\frac{1}{R_{3A}C_3}\int V_{e2}\,dt - \frac{1}{R_{3B}C_3}\int -V_{e1}\,dt$$

where

$$R_{3A}C_3 = \frac{a_{e2}L_{12}}{a_{i21}} \qquad R_{3B}C_3 = \frac{a_{e1}L_{12}}{a_{i21}}$$

R_{12} *Simulator*

$$-V_{iR} = -\frac{R_{4C}}{R_{4A}}V_{e2} - \frac{R_{4C}}{R_{4B}}(-V_{e1})$$

where

$$\frac{R_{4C}}{R_{4A}} = \frac{a_{i21}}{a_{e2}R_{12}} \qquad \frac{R_{4C}}{R_{4B}} = \frac{a_{i21}}{a_{e1}R_{12}}$$

and

$$V_{i21} = V_{iL} + V_{iR}$$

C_{01} *Simulator*

$$-V_{e1} = -\frac{1}{R_5C_5}\int V_{i21}\,dt \quad \text{where } R_5C_5 = \frac{a_{i21}C_{01}}{a_{e1}}$$

(4.68)

The interconnections of the direct simulators are shown in Fig. 4.24(b) where one adder and one sign reverser are also needed to take account of signs. Potentiometers could be used as an alternative method of scaling. As already stated, the main advantage of this approach is the direct correspondence between elements and variables in the original network and their corresponding simulated counterparts.

A modification is necessary to the direct interconnection of direct simulators for a junction of three or more similar elements. This aspect is discussed in Reference 18.

REFERENCES

1. 'Models and Analogies for demonstrating Electrical Principles', *Engineer*, 1926, **142**, Parts I–XIX.

2. F. M. ROGERS: 'Demonstration Experiments: Mechanical Analogs of Electric Circuits', *Amer. J. Phys.*, 1946, **14**, p. 318.

3. G. G. BLAKE: 'A Mechanical Model Analogous to an Oscillatory Electrical Circuit', *Engineer*, 1946, **181**, p. 535.

4. C. A. NICKLE: 'Oscillographic Solution of Electromechanical Systems', *Trans. A.I.E.E.*, 1925, **44**, p. 844.

5. W. W. SOROKA: *Analog Methods in Computation and Simulation* (McGraw-Hill, 1954).

6. F. A. FIRESTONE: 'A New Analogy between Mechanical and Electrical Systems', *J. Acoust. Soc. Amer.*, 1933, **4**, p. 249.

7. H. M. TRENT: 'Isomorphisms between Orientated Linear Graphs and Lumped Physical System', *J. Acoust. Soc. Amer.*, 1955, **27**, p. 500.

8. W. J. KARPLUS: *Analog Simulation* (McGraw-Hill, 1958).

9. H. F. OLSON: *Dynamical Analogies* (Van Nostrand, 1943).

10. M. F. GARDNER and J. L. BARNES: *Transients in Linear Systems* (Chapman & Hall, 1945).

11. H. E. KOENIG and W. A. BLACKWELL: *Electromechanical System Theory* (McGraw-Hill, 1961).

12. B. D. H. TELLEGEN: 'The Gyrator, a New Electric Network Element', *Phil. Res. Reps*, 1948, **3**, p. 81.

13. H. SIRE DE VILAR: 'La Dualité in Électrotechnique', *L'Éclairage Électrique*, 1901, **27**, pp. 252 and 278.

14. R. J. A. PAUL: 'Review of Analogue Computing Techniques', *I. Mech. E, Symposium—The Use of Computers in Mechanical Engineering, 1962*, Paper 1. p. 5.

15. G. F. PASKUSZ and B. BUSSELL: 'Circuit Theory in a Unified Curriculum', I.R.E. Prof. Group on Education, 1960, E3, p. 84.

16. N. W. MCLACHLAN: *Complex Variable Theory and Transform Calculus* (Cambridge University Press, 1955).

17. R. J. A. PAUL: 'Two-Port Network Representation of D.C. Electro-Mechanical Transducers', College of Aeronautics Note No. 121, 1962.

18. V. L. LARROWE: 'Direct Simulation', *Control Engineering*, 1954, **1**, p. 25.

Chapter 5

ITERATIVE OPERATION OF THE ANALOGUE
COMPUTER

5.1 THE INTEGRATOR USED AS A MEMORY DEVICE

THE ELECTRONIC ANALOGUE INTEGRATOR IS ESSENTIALLY AN
energy storage device in which the feedback capacitor stores electrostatic
energy. If the supply of energy to the capacitor is suddenly terminated by
open-circuiting the input circuit, as shown in Fig. 5.1, we have the 'hold'
condition as described in Chapter 2. The potential difference across the
capacitor, at the instant of opening the switch, would remain at this value

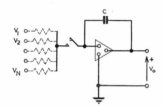

Fig. 5.1 *Integrator in 'hold' condition*

for all future time provided that the leakage resistance across the capacitor
was infinite and the amplifier had zero input leakage current and zero
offset voltage. In practice, the capacitor has a finite leakage resistance and
the amplifier has finite leakage current and offset voltage. However, as
discussed in Chapter 2, the effect of these imperfections may be minimized
by careful design and the use of good quality components so that the
resultant error, i.e. the change in capacitor voltage over a certain period,
is within a tolerable figure. The integrator, in the 'hold' condition, is thus
acting as a memory device. In the normal operation of an analogue
computer, all control operations are carried out simultaneously, i.e.
synchronously, and the memory capabilities of the integrator are not fully
utilized. If now the synchronous control of the integrators is replaced by
asynchronous control in which, at any instant, some integrators are in the
'hold' condition, some in the 'compute' condition and some in the
're-set' condition, then the storage capabilities of the integrators may be

used so that the computer can tackle a wider class of problems than that possible with synchronous control.

A typical integrator circuit is shown in Fig. 5.2 where the signals $(V_1, V_2 \ldots V_N)$ represent the input variables, V_o represents the output variable and V_{IC} represents the initial condition voltage. With contact A_1

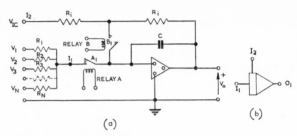

Fig. 5.2   *Typical integrator circuit*

(a) *Circuit*   (b) *Symbolic notation*

open, B_1 closed and a constant voltage V_{IC} applied, we have the 'initial condition' or 're-set' mode where the output voltage rises exponentially in value as shown in Fig. 5.3

i.e. $$-V_o(t) = V_{IC}(1-\varepsilon^{-t/R_iC}) \qquad (5.1)$$

If $t/R_i C \geqq 10$, the output voltage approaches the input voltage V_{IC} (with a reversal in sign) within an accuracy of better than $0{\cdot}005\%$.

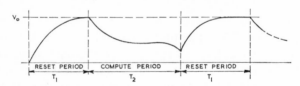

Fig. 5.3   *Output voltage during 'reset' and 'compute' periods*

For the 'compute' mode, contact B_1 is opened and contact A_1 closed and thus the integrator integrates the input variables to give a solution which may be typically of the form shown in Fig. 5.3, over the period T_2. If this sequence of operations is repeated we have repetitive operation of the integrators (see Chapter 2).

Now consider the situation illustrated in Fig. 5.4 where a second integrator, acting as a memory, is in the 're-set' condition and is connected to the output of the first integrator through the 'initial condition' input. The second integrator will track or follow its input voltage (with a finite time delay) to give an output voltage which is approximately $-V_o$. If the B relay contacts of the second integrator are suddenly opened at a given value of V_o as shown in Fig. 5.4, the output of the second integrator will subsequently remain at this value for the remainder of the compute period. In other words it is acting as a memory device and this facility permits iterative solutions of problems. Before discussing this aspect we shall consider a typical form of asynchronous control of the integrators.

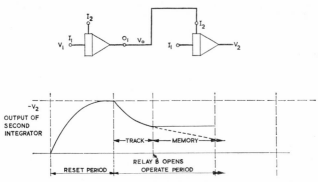

Fig. 5.4 *Coupled integrators*

5.2 ASYNCHRONOUS CONTROL OF INTEGRATOR OPERATION

The concept of 'sample and hold' for the solution of problems on the analogue computer is not new and a typical application was described by Wang[1] in 1952. A commercial version of this type of control was first introduced in 1958[2,3] and a typical control sequence[4] is shown in Fig. 5.5.

The operating modes are the same as for synchronous control, i.e. 'standby', 'initial condition' (IC), 'hold' (H) and 'compute'. It should be noted that all computing units with the exception of integrators are mode independent and attention is therefore restricted to integrator mode control. With reference to Fig. 5.5 an integrator operating in the repetitive mode is denoted by 'R' and one operating in the complementary repetitive mode is denoted by '$\overline{R}$'. It will be noted that whenever an 'R' integrator is in the compute mode an '$\overline{R}$' integrator is in the initial condition mode and conversely, with the exception of the first cycle of operation. During this first cycle the first set of initial conditions are set manually on the R integrator and in this initial condition mode the $\overline{R}$ integrators are in the 'hold' mode in order to prevent possible overloading of the latter. The 'hold' period is provided between each pair of 'initial condition' and 'compute' intervals to allow sufficient time for information transfer between R and $\overline{R}$ integrators and to avoid relay tracking difficulties.

The control modes for the integrator acting as a memory M or as a complementary memory $\overline{M}$ are also shown in Fig. 5.5, where it will be noted that the integrator is essentially either in the IC mode or H mode. For this type of operation the input terminal is not used and is open-circuited.

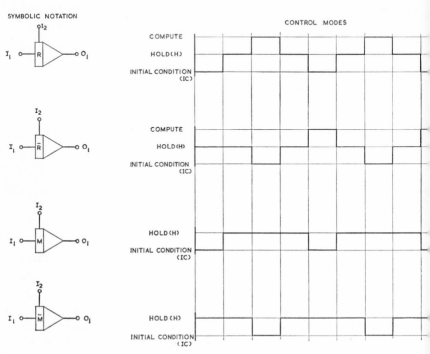

Fig. 5.5 *Asynchronous control modes*
Refer to Fig. 5.2

Hold mode A_1 open B_1 open
Compute mode A_1 closed B_1 open
IC mode A_1 open B_1 closed

In a practical installation, the 'compute', 'hold' and 'initial condition' periods may be controlled independently and different rates of control sequences for different sets of integrators may be incorporated. This facility is necessary in some problems where it is desired to have an iterative method of solution for one or more variables at a certain iteration rate, and to have a different iteration rate for other variables. In some problems it is required to store the value of a problem variable when one or more other variables reach a certain value or are coincident. For this application,

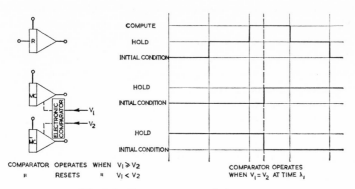

COMPARATOR OPERATES WHEN $V_1 \geqslant V_2$
" RESETS " $V_1 < V_2$

COMPARATOR OPERATES
WHEN $V_1 = V_2$ AT TIME λ_1

Fig. 5.6 *Comparator-controlled memories*

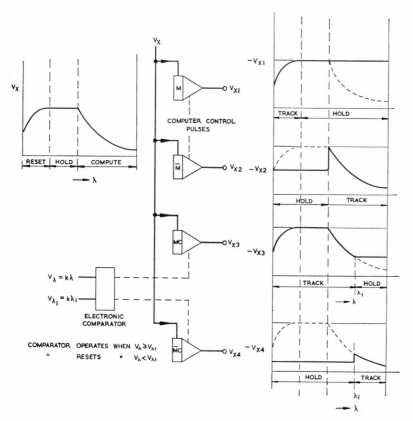

Fig. 5.7 *Four basic forms of memory*

133

the integrator switching is controlled by an electronic comparator as shown in Fig. 5.6. Two voltages, V_1 and V_2 representing problem variables, are applied to the comparator which operates when $V_1 = V_2$ so that the memory denoted as MC is switched from the 'initial condition' mode to the 'hold' mode and the comparator controlled memory in the complementary mode, denoted as $\overline{\text{MC}}$, is switched from the 'hold' condition to the 'initial condition' mode.

The four basic types of memories are summarized in Fig. 5.7.

5.3 BASIC ARRANGEMENTS OF MEMORIES

(i) *Ratchet circuit*

A tandem pair comprising a complementary memory $\overline{\text{M}}$ and a memory M, as shown in Fig. 5.8(a), provides a means for memorizing a value in one computing cycle which may be used in the next cycle. Memory M stores a value of a computing variable, say X_n, which may be used through an entire cycle for calculation of X_{n+1}. The latter value will be memorized at the start of the next re-set period to provide X_{n+1} in the succeding computing period for calculation of X_{n+2}, etc. The arrangement shown in Fig. 5.8(a) is sometimes called a ratchet circuit and finds application in sequential calculations which are performed in synchronism with the computer.

(ii) *Transform circuit*

The memory pair shown in Fig. 5.8(b), consisting of comparator controlled memories MC and $\overline{\text{MC}}$, may be used for the solution of a wide class of problems including the cases of multiple integration, ordinary and partial differential equations (with or without split boundaries) and transformation of a variable which is a function of time to a function of a dependent variable. It is this latter facility which is the essential capability of the circuit and hence the name 'transform circuit'. Referring to Fig. 5.8(b), memory MC tracks a particular computing variable until the comparator operates at which instant the value in MC is stored. Memory $\overline{\text{MC}}$ then tracks this value and when it is attained the memory may be switched to 'hold' and memory MC used to track a new value of the computing variable. The sequence of operations may then be repeated in this iterative fashion. Specifically, if V_1 represents a repetitive ramp function, V_3 is a function of V_1, i.e. $f(V_1)$, and V_2 represents a function of a dependent variable say $g(x)$, then MC tracks $f(V_1)$. Upon coincidence of two comparator voltages, both memories are triggered locking the MC memory on the value $f(V_1)$ when V_1 is equal to $g(x)$. The $\overline{\text{MC}}$ memory stores this value, which is now effectively $f[g(x)]$, and makes it available as the final output. To establish a point of comparison between the ramp function and the dependent variable $g(x)$ it is necessary for the ramp to sweep between the minimum and maximum possible values of the latter in one repetitive computing period. The generation of this ramp function may be achieved

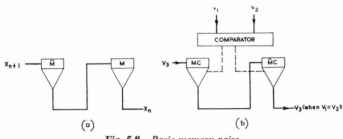

Fig. 5.8 *Basic memory pairs*

(a) *Rachet circuit*   (b) *Transform circuit*

by an integrator, with an initial condition of maximum computer voltage (say $+100\,\text{V}$). At the start of each computing period a negative voltage is connected at the input of this integrator, so that the integrator output voltage changes from $-100\,\text{V}$ to $+100\,\text{V}$ in the computing period.

5.4 TIME-SCALE EXPANSION—RADAR AIMING PROBLEM[5]

The problem is a simple trajectory calculation from which data are obtained to aim a shipboard radar beam at a missile throughout its calculated trajectory.

The solution time is assumed to be of the order of 500 seconds and this rules out the possibility of using conventional electronic analogue techniques due to the excessive drift errors which would arise over this period.

Drift and noise errors may be reduced by iteration which provides solution of the entire flight path several times a second. The situation is illustrated in Fig. 5.9 in which the simulated trajectory is solved in a repetitive manner, several times a second, and these solutions are fed to an integrator acting as a memory.

A ramp voltage signal, of the form $V_1 = kNt$, generated repetitively from the computer over the period T_i is compared in the comparator with another ramp signal of the form $V_2 = kt$ where k is a constant, T_i is the computing period of each repetitive solution and t is real time.

When $V_1 \geq V_2$ for each repetitive solution, the comparator operates memories MC and $\overline{\text{MC}}$ of the transform pair so that MC holds the value of V_0 (altitude) at this instant of coincidence. This hold condition persists until $V_1 < V_2$ at which instant MC again tracks V_0. During this intervening period memory $\overline{MC}$ tracks the value held in MC. The sequence of operations is shown in Fig. 5.9. These iterative up-dated samples are fed continuously to the shipboard radar throughout the flight of the missile.

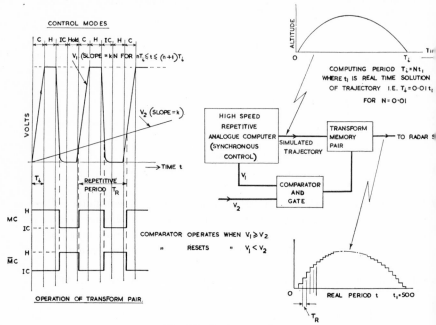

Fig. 5.9 *Trajectory solution*

In this way the analogue computer may be used to provide accurate solutions over large computing periods, or in other words the dynamic operating range of the machine has been extended considerably by the use of iterative techniques.

5.5 EVALUATION OF A DEFINITE INTEGRAL[2]

The problem is to evaluate the integral of one or more variables in repetitive operation at definite and sometimes variable limits. A typical example is the minimization of some performance index in a control system by altering design parameters. The method proposed in Reference 2 is shown in Fig. 5.10 for the evaluation of the function z, where

$$z = \int_0^\alpha f(x, y)\, dx \qquad (5.2)$$

The variable 'x' is represented by the independent computer time variable. With scale factors

$$V_{z,0} = a_{z,0} z \quad V_{y,0} = a_{y,0} y \quad V_{x,0} = a_{x,0} x \quad \text{and} \quad \lambda = a_\lambda x$$

where λ is the independent computer time variable, we have

$$V_{z,0} = a_{z,0} \int_0^{a_\lambda \alpha} f\left(\frac{V_{x,0}}{a_{x,0}}, \frac{V_{y,0}}{a_{y,0}}\right) \frac{d\lambda}{a_\lambda}$$

$$= \int_0^\beta g(V_{x,0}, V_{y,0}) \, d\lambda \tag{5.3}$$

where

$$\beta = a_\lambda \alpha \quad \frac{a_{z,0}}{a_\lambda} f\left(\frac{V_{x,0}}{a_{x,0}}, \frac{V_{y,0}}{a_{y,0}}\right) = g(V_{x,0}, V_{y,0})$$

The function $g(V_{x,0}, V_{y,0})$ is fed to integrator 1 in which the appropriate initial condition voltage $V_{z,0}(0) = a_{z,0} z_0$ is set. The output of this integrator is $-\int_0^\lambda g(V_{x,0}, V_{y,0}) \, d\lambda$. A constant voltage A is fed to integrator

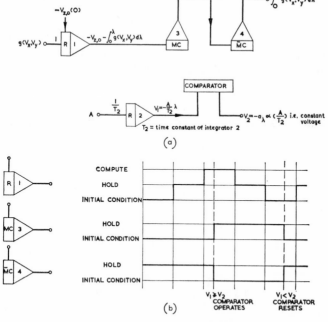

Fig. 5.10 *Evaluation of a definite integral*

(a) *Computing arrangement*   (b) *Control modes*

2 which produces an output voltage $V_1 = - A\lambda/T_2$ and this is compared in the comparator with the constant voltage $V_2 = - a_\lambda \alpha A/T_2$.

Both integrators are operated repetitively and when coincidence occurs, when $V_2 = V_1$, memory MC3 tracking the output of integrator 1 is switched to the 'hold' condition and memory MC4 tracks and stores this value of the integral at coincidence, i.e. when $\lambda = a_\lambda \alpha$. The result is that MC4 has as its output the previous value of the definite integral from 0 to β from each preceding cycle. If desired, the limit of integration, β, may be changed from cycle to cycle in accordance with the desired problem solution. The control modes are also shown in Fig. 5.10.

5.6 MULTIPLE INTEGRATION[2]

A typical example is the evaluation of the volume of a cylinder with varying radius. This volume is the double integration with respect to radius r and length x.

The radius as a function of x, i.e. $r(x)$ is obtained from a function generator. The situation is illustrated in Fig. 5.11.

If we denote the volume by ϕ

$$\phi = 2\pi \int_0^{x_1} \int_0^{r_w} r\, dr\, dx \tag{5.4}$$

where r_w represents the radius of the wall. We identify x as the computer independent variable λ and specify the following scale factors

$$V_r = a_r r \quad V_\phi = a_\phi \phi \quad V_x = a_x x \quad \lambda = 1 \times x$$

We assume that r may be expressed repetitively in the form

$$r = k_r \lambda^*$$

i.e.
$$V_r = a_r k_r \lambda^* \tag{5.5}$$

where λ^* denotes repetitive time. This gives the computing equation

$$V_\phi = \frac{2\pi a_\phi k_r}{a_r} \int_0^{\lambda_1} \int_0^{\lambda_w^*} V_r\, d\lambda\, d\lambda^*$$

i.e.
$$V_\phi = \frac{1}{T_6} \int_0^{\lambda_1} d\lambda \left\{ \frac{1}{T_3} \int_0^{\lambda_w^*} V_r\, d\lambda^* \right\} \tag{5.6}$$

when
$$T_3 = \frac{a_r}{2\pi k_r} \quad T_6 = \frac{1}{a_\phi}$$

The computing arrangement shown in Fig. 5.11 is derived from equation (5.6) and the total computing period is $\lambda = \lambda_1$. Integrators 2 and 3 are operated repetitively and the remaining integrators in a non-repetitive mode. V_x is generated at the output of integrator 1 and fed to the function generator which gives an output $f(\lambda) = V_{r_w}$. The latter signal is connected

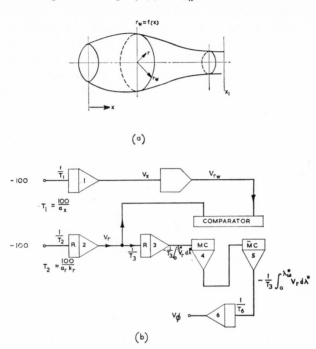

(a)

(b)

Fig. 5.11 *Evaluation of the volume of a cylinder*

(a) *Cylinder*

$$\text{Volume} \quad \phi = \int_0^{x_1} \int_0^{r_w} 2\pi r \, dr \, dx$$

(b) *Computing diagram*

to a comparator and when its value is equal to the value of V_r, during each repetitive cycle, the comparator puts memory MC4, which was tracking

the output of 3, into hold. The value held is then $+\dfrac{1}{T_3}\displaystyle\int_0^{\lambda_w^*} V_r \, d\lambda^*$. This

value is now tracked and stored in the complementary memory $\overline{\text{MC}}5$ and fed to integrator 6 which gives at its output the required double integral. The output of $\overline{\text{MC}}5$ is thus always the previous value of the cross-sectional area of the wall and if the repetition period is small compared with the period λ_1 the quantization error may be made negligible.

Although this multiple integration is relatively trivial the same procedure may be adopted for more complicated functions. A typical application is the solution of temperature gradients in a fixed-bed chemical reactor operating under steady state conditions.

In the above example the radial function $R = f(r)$ must be solved automatically by the computer in repetitive operations. The value of R is known at the wall while dR/dr is known at the centre of the cylinder where the radius is zero. The procedure outlined is therefore an illustration of the method of reducing a split-boundary value problem in R to an initial condition problem.

5.7 SPLIT-BOUNDARY VALUE PROBLEM[6]

Consider the equation
$$\frac{d^2 y}{dx^2} = -y \tag{5.7}$$

with boundary conditions
$$\frac{dy}{dx} = 0 \quad \text{for } x = 0$$

$$y = y_L \quad \text{for } x = L$$

Assume the following scale factors
$$\lambda = a_\lambda x \quad V_{y,0} = a_{y,0}\, y \quad V_{y,1} = a_{y,1}\frac{dy}{dx}$$

where λ is the independent computer time variable.

Hence
$$\frac{dy}{dx} = -\int y\, dx$$

i.e.
$$V_{y,1} = -\frac{a_{y,1}}{a_{y,0}\, a_\lambda}\int V_{y,0}\, d\lambda$$

i.e.
$$V_{y,1} = -\frac{1}{T_{y,1}}\int V_{y,0}\, d\lambda \tag{5.8}$$

where
$$T_{y,1} = \frac{a_{y,0}\, a_\lambda}{a_{y,1}} = T_1$$

Initial Conditions $V_{y,1}(0) = 0$

Final Conditions $V_{y,0} = a_{y,0} y_L \quad \text{for } \lambda = a_\lambda L$

The trial and error procedure adopted for the solution of this equation is to assume a value for y_0 and solve the equation. The resulting value of y_L is compared with the given value of y_L, a new value of y_0 is assumed and the calculations repeated if the two values do not match.

The computing diagram is shown in Fig. 5.12 where amplifiers 1, 2 and 3, operating repetitively about 10 times a second, solve equation (5.8). The first cycle has initial conditions $V_{y,1} = 0$; $V_{y,0} = 0$ and when $\lambda = L$, the

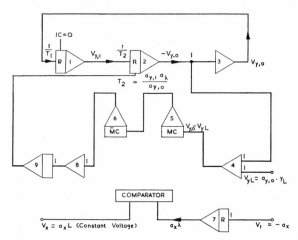

Fig. 5.12 *Solution of split boundary problem*

comparator operates and memory $\overline{M}C5$ tracks and stores the value of $V_{y,0}(L) - V_{yL}$ which is now held in $\overline{M}C6$. The output of $\overline{M}C6$ is integrated in integrator 9 (non-repetitive operation) to give an output

$$(V_{y,0}(L) - V_{yL}) \Delta\lambda$$

where $\Delta\lambda$ is the time period between coincidence of the comparator and the next initial condition mode of the repetitive cycle. This voltage is used as the trial initial condition for integrator 2, for the next computing period. In this way we have a trial intial condition change given by the equation

$$^n\Delta V_{y,0}(0) = [^{n-1}V_{y,0}(L) - V_{yL}]\Delta\lambda_n \qquad (5.9)$$

for the nth cycle where $V_{y,0}(0) = 0$. This process converges rapidly to the desired solution when there is no significant change in the initial condition of integrator 2.

5.8 CONTINUOUS MEMORY[2]

Several applications arise which require the storage of a complete function of a variable as distinct from the storage of one value of the function. This type of memory is the so-called *continuous memory* and may be derived from combinations of the memory pairs already described. The most common requirement for this facility is illustrated by the variation of $f(x)$ with the solution curves (i), (ii), (iii), etc. in Fig. 5.13. The function F_1 for $f(x)$ is required as input to the computer circuit to predict F_2 for the subsequent operating cycle. In the subsequent operating cycle the values of F_2 will be required to calculate F_3 and so on. The memory circuit is based on Newton's Forward Interpolation Formula which states that the values of $f(x)$ at equal values of x may be used to express $f(x)$ as a function of x in the form of a polynomial equation

i.e.
$$f(x) = A + B(x) + \frac{C(x)(x-1)}{2!} + \frac{D}{3!}(x)(x-1)(x-2) + ... \quad (5.10)$$

The values of coefficients A, B, C and D are derived from the differences shown in Table 5.1. Thus, if the values $f(x_a)$, $f(x_b)$, $f(x_c)$ and $f(x_d)$, etc. are known, they may be used as the inputs to a summing network to give outputs representing the coefficients of A, B, C and D, etc. Simultaneously

TABLE 5.1—NEWTON'S DIFFERENCE ARRAY

x	$f(x)$	Δ	Δ^2	Δ^3	
a	2				$f(a) = \quad 2 = A$
		10			
b	12		3		$\Delta_a = \quad 10 = B$
		13		-1	
c	25		2		$\Delta_a{}^2 = \quad 3 = C$
		15			
d	40				$\Delta_a{}^3 = -1 = D$

the value of x may be used in a function generator to give the required products x, $x-1$, $x-2$, etc. A simple case for four points is given in Table 5.1. One simple arrangement is shown in Fig. 5.13(c) in which the required values of $f(x)$ for curve (i) may be retained in memory while new values for curve (ii) are learned for the subsequent cycle. For the case shown in Table 5.1 four pairs of MC and $\overline{\text{M}}$C memories are used. During

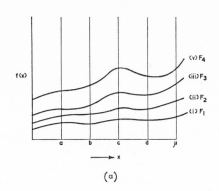

(a)

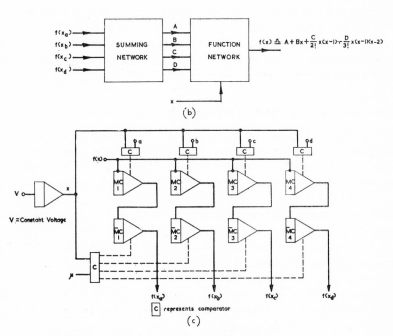

(b)

(c)

Fig. 5.13 *Unscaled diagram for continuous memory*

(a) *Function of x*   (b) *Basic computing blocks for generation*
    of polynomial   (c) *Continuous memory circuit*

143

the first cycle the values of $f(x_a)$, $f(x_b)$, $f(x_c)$ and $f(x_d)$, for curve (i), are present at the outputs of the $\overline{MC}$ memories, and these are fed to the summing network to produce the coefficients A, B, C and D which are used in the development of the curve F_2 as x varies. At the same time the respective MC memories have relay comparators which open the first memory when x is equal to a, the second memory when x is equal to b, the third when x is equal to c and the fourth when x is equal to d. As the MC memories are fed by the computer with the calculated curve F_2, at the end of the cycle the values of $f(x_a)$, $f(x_b)$, $f(x_c)$ and $f(x_d)$ for curve F_2 are held in the respective MC memories. It is necessary to transfer these values to the $\overline{MC}$ memories for use in the subsequent cycle and this is carried out at the end of the current compute period. This is accomplished by one common comparator circuit that switches all four $\overline{MC}$ memories when the value of x is equal to μ, which is a value greater than x_d.

In Fig. 5.13, scale factors are not incorporated in order to simplify the explanation of the process.

Four terms of the Newton formula were used in the above discussion but, in practice, it may be necessary to use more terms particularly in curves with large changes in slope.

5.9 FUNCTION GENERATION

As mentioned in Chapter 2, the normal complement of an analogue computer includes various forms of function generators, e.g. multipliers, arbitrary function generators of one or more dependent variables and units to simulate transportation lag (dead-time). Other specialized units are usually provided including those based on the use of non-linear diodes to simulate switching functions and common non-linear effects such as dead zone, limiting, hysteresis and backlash.

The generation of a function of the independent variable (i.e. time) may be obtained, usually without the need for special units, by solving implicitly the appropriate analytic function.

The reader who is interested in the methods employed for the construction and applications of these devices, is referred to more comprehensive texts such as References 7 and 8.

This limitation of the conventional electronic analogue computer in respect of function generation, which has already been mentioned, has created a need for more versatile methods to generate functions of one or more dependent variables. This has resulted in the introduction of hybrid methods of computation (combined analogue/digital techniques) and a recent review concerned with this aspect is given in Reference 9.

An alternative approach, for more specific functions, is to use iterative methods. This method, although restricted in accuracy, does not require the use of specialized units other than those already described in this chapter. This facility of generating a function of a dependent variable is achieved by the transform circuit described in Section 5.3, in which may be effected the transformation of a function of time (generated repetitively at a high rate) into a function of a dependent variable for discrete samples of x. The basic approach will be illustrated by describing two simple examples.

(i) *Generation of* $f(x) = a + bx + cx^2 + dx^3$,

where a, b, c and d are constants.

The computing diagram is shown in Fig. 5.14, from which the following relationships may be established,

i.e.
$$+V_1 = +100\left(1 - \frac{t}{T}\right) \qquad (5.11)$$

With $t/T = 2$ the value of V_1 ranges from -100V to $+100$V to cope with all possible values of x, with which it is compared in the comparators.

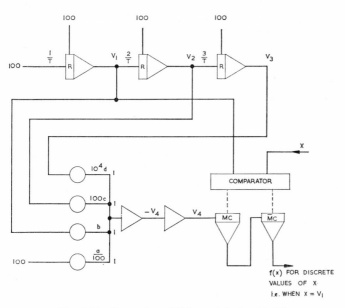

Fig. 5.14 *Generation of* $f(x) = a + bx + cx^2 + dx^3$
(Repetitive computing period $= 2T$)

145

Also
$$V_2 = 100\left(1 - \frac{2t}{T} + \frac{t^2}{T^2}\right)$$

$$= 100\left(1 - \frac{t}{T}\right)^2 = \frac{V_1^2}{100} \tag{5.12}$$

$$+V_3 = 100\left(1 - \frac{3t}{T} + \frac{3t^2}{T^2} - \frac{t^3}{T^3}\right)$$

i.e.
$$V_3 = 100\left(1 - \frac{t}{T}\right)^3 = \frac{V_1^3}{10^4} \tag{5.13}$$

and
$$V_4 = (a + bV_1 + 100cV_2 + 10^4\,dV_3)$$

i.e.
$$V_4 = (a + bV_1 + cV_1^2 + dV_1^3) \tag{5.14}$$

Now the comparator of the transform circuit operates each time that $x = V_1$. At these instants the value of V_4, which is tracked in MC, is transferred to the $\overline{\text{MC}}$ store to give an output representing $f(x)$ at these instants.

Note: It has been assumed that all the constants have positive sign but only a slight modification is necessary to take account of different signs.

(ii) *Generation of $f(x) = x^a$,*

where a is a positive constant.[10]

It is assumed that the variable x is always positive and is identified as $100\varepsilon^{-t/T}$, where T is a positive integer used for time-scaling.

The function $100\varepsilon^{-t/T}$ is generated at a high repetitive rate, where the computing period is $2T$, by solving the equation,

$$\frac{dV_1}{dt} + \frac{V_1}{T} = 0 \tag{5.15}$$

with initial condition $V_1 = 100$ at $t = 0$. The function $100^a\,\varepsilon^{-at/T}$ is generated in a similar manner by solving the equation

$$\frac{dV_2}{dt} + \frac{aV_2}{T} = 0 \tag{5.16}$$

with initial condition $V_2 = 100^a$ at $t = 0$, where a is assumed to be less than unity. $100^a\,\varepsilon^{-at/T}$ may be expressed as

$$100^a\,\varepsilon^{-at/T} = (100\,\varepsilon^{-t/T})^a \equiv x^a \tag{5.17}$$

Referring to the computing diagram in Fig. 5.15, the transform circuit operates at each instant when $V_1 = 100\varepsilon^{-t/T} = x$, and thus the output of MC represents $f(x)$ at these instants.

In Reference 10 methods are described for electronic resolving and generation of sines and cosines, based on iterative techniques. The main

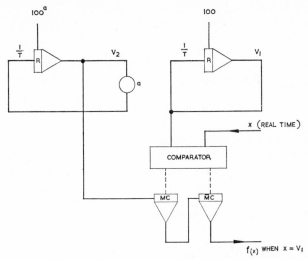

Fig. 5.15 *Generator of $f(x) = x^a$ (positive values of x only)*
(Note: 'a' assumed to be less than unity; repetitive computing period = 2T)

limitation on this approach is the necessity for a high repetition rate so that enough samples, for a given accuracy, may be obtained of the sampled variable.

5.10 AN OPTIMIZATION PROBLEM[11]

A general statement of the problem is to maximize (or minimize) an objective function

$$F = F(x_1, x_2, ..., x_m, y_1, y_2, ..., y_n) \tag{5.18}$$

subject to the constraints

$$\alpha_i = \alpha_i(x_1, x_2, ..., x_m, y_1, y_2, ..., y_n) \geq \beta_i \tag{5.19}$$

where $x_1, x_2, ..., x_m$ represent the independent variables $y_1, y_2, ..., y_n$ represent the dependent variables and β_i are constant and/or functions of the variables.

147

Typically F may be a profit function to be maximized or alternatively a cost function to be minimized.

The method of attack is based on the assumption that a functional relationship between the independent and dependent variables is known. In particular. this would be represented by the simulation of the basic set of differential equations representing the system under investigation. It therefore follows that the dependent variables may be eliminated from equations (5.18) and (5.19) to give an objective function of the form

$$G = G(x_1, x_2, ..., x_m) \qquad (5.20)$$

and constraints of the form

$$\gamma_i = \gamma_i(x_1, x_2, ..., x_m) \qquad (5.21)$$

Neglecting, for the moment, consideration of the constraints, the maximum rate of increase of G may be achieved by varying the x_j proportions to their corresponding elements in the gradient of G, i.e. the gradient of G is

$$\nabla G = \left(\frac{\partial G}{\partial x_1}, \frac{\partial G}{\partial x_2}, \frac{\partial G}{\partial x_j}, ..., \frac{\partial G}{\partial x_m} \right)$$

so $(x_1, x_2, ..., x_j, ..., x_m)$ are to be differentially incremented in direct proportion to the elements in ∇G, respectively. This is the 'steepest ascent' principle.

If Δx_j is very small,

then
$$\frac{\Delta G}{\Delta x_j} \simeq \frac{\partial G}{\partial x_j} \quad \text{for } j = 1...m \qquad (5.22)$$

Consider the maximization of G with respect to one variable say x_1. If the simulator is operated repetitively, and the value of x_1 input to the simulator is varied continuously in a slower time frame-of-reference, then x_1 may be considered to be essentially constant during one simulator cycle. At the end of this cycle, $\Delta G / \Delta x_1$ may be calculated from the values of G and x_1 found in this cycle and the previous cycle. The value of $\Delta G / \Delta x_1$ may then be used to slowly alter x_1 during the next cycle according to the relationship,

$$x_1(\text{next cycle}) = x_1(\text{current cycle}) + \int_0^{\lambda_i} \delta \left(\frac{\Delta G}{\Delta x_1} \right) d\lambda \qquad (5.23)$$

where δ is an arbitrary constant (step size) and λ_i is the time for one repetitive operation. In this way x_1 is automatically adjusted in the correct direction until $\Delta G/\Delta x_1$ is zero, at which time x_1 will remain constant. Thus for the general case, $\Delta G/\Delta x_j$ will equal zero when either a stationary state is obtained or x_j becomes limited.

The above procedure may be extended to several variables by varying each x_j in turn with respect to repetitive computer cycles. For example with three variables x_1, x_2 and x_3, in cycle N, x_1 is varied and the resulting $\Delta G/\Delta x_1|_N$ is stored in the analogue memory. In cycle $N+1$, x_2 is varied and $\Delta G/\Delta x_2|_{N+1}$ is stored. Finally in cycle $N+2$, x_3 is varied and $\Delta G/\Delta x_3|_{N+2}$ is stored. This sequence of events is now repeated so that in cycle $N+3$, x_1 is driven with $\Delta G/\Delta x_1|_N$ and the resulting $\Delta G/\Delta x_1|_{N+3}$ is stored; in cycle $N+4$, x_2 is driven with $\Delta G/\Delta x_2|_{N+1}$ and so on. This iterative process will terminate when all $\Delta G/\Delta x_j = 0$. A further point of interest is that the system will be stable since any disturbance will cause the variables to be automatically adjusted to values corresponding to the stationary state.

The functional constraint γ may be imposed on the system as follows. During the maximization of G an electronic comparator may be used to monitor $\gamma - \beta$. When $\gamma - \beta < 0$ the electronic comparator operates so that $(\gamma - \beta)$ is substituted for G and the optimization circuits operate to increase $(\gamma - \beta)$ until $(\gamma - \beta) \geqq 0$, at which point the electronic comparator replaces $(\gamma - \beta)$ with G. The system will oscillate about a constrained optimum and, since δ in equation (5.23) may be made very small, the magnitude of these oscillations may be decreased to essentially the noise level of the computer.

It appears that more than one functional constraint may be imposed by extension of the above logic. However, as these increase in number the optimization procedure may occupy an intolerable time.

A practical application of this approach is given in Reference 11 where a chemical process plant, for naptha reforming, is considered.

5.11 SPLIT-BOUNDARY PROBLEM—EXPERIMENTAL RESULTS

Two split-boundary value problems were investigated on a new iterative analogue machine developed at the College of Aeronautics, Cranfield.[12]
(a) The problem described in Section 5.7 with the computing diagram shown in Fig. 5.12 was first considered and the results obtained are shown in Fig. 5.16. In these initial investigations it was found that the problem solution was very sensitive to a time delay in the comparator-controlled memory operation and to change in initial condition value. This emphasizes the need for fast integrator mode switching and for accurate setting of fixed values of initial conditions. For comparator-controlled memories it would appear that solid-state switching is essential since the delay of electromechanical relays (say 1–2 ms) can cause a significant error in the

solution. The results shown in Fig. 5.16 are within about 1% of the correct values and this error was mainly due to relay switching time.

(b) Uniformly loaded beam

The problem considered is that of the beam shown in Fig. 5.17(a) where l is the length and w is the loading per unit length.

We have
$$EI\frac{d^4y}{dx^4} = w \tag{5.24}$$

where E = Young's Modulus, I = moment of inertia, y the vertical deflection and x the horizontal distance from left-hand support.

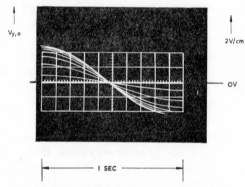

Fig. 5.16 *Solution of split boundary value problem* (*Refering to* Fig. 5.12)

$T_1 = 1\cdot0 \qquad T_2 = 0\cdot1 \qquad y_L = 10$
$a_{y,1} = 0\cdot1 \qquad a_{y,1} = 1\cdot0 \qquad a_\lambda = 1\cdot0 \qquad a_x = 10$
Repetition rate $= 1\cdot0\,\text{s}$
$V_{y,0}(0) = 12\cdot35$ *theoretical*
$V_{y,0}(0) = 12\cdot46$ *measured*

The boundary conditions are:

$$y = \frac{dy}{dx} = 0 \quad \text{at } x = 0$$

$$y = \frac{dy}{dx} = 0 \quad \text{at } x = l$$

The solution is given by

$$EIy = \frac{w}{24}x^2(l-x)^2 \tag{5.25}$$

150

The maximum deflection occurs at $x = l/2$ and is given by

$$y = \frac{wl^4}{384EI}$$

We may adopt the following scale factors

$$\lambda = a_\lambda x$$

$$V_{y,4} = a_{y,4}\frac{d^4y}{dx^4} \quad V_{y,3} = a_{y,3}\frac{d^3y}{dx^3} \quad V_{y,2} = a_{y,2}\frac{d^2y}{dx^2}$$

$$V_{y,1} = a_{y,1}\frac{dy}{dx} \quad V_{y,0} = a_{y,0}\,y$$

Substituting into equation (5.24) we have the computing equation

$$V_{y,4} = \frac{w}{EI}a_{y,4} \qquad (5.26)$$

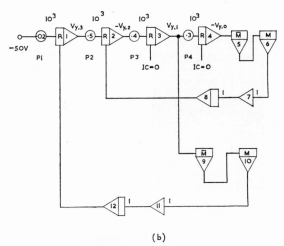

(a)

(b)

Fig. 5.17 *Beam problem*

(a) *Encastré beam with uniform load*   (b) *Computing diagram*

151

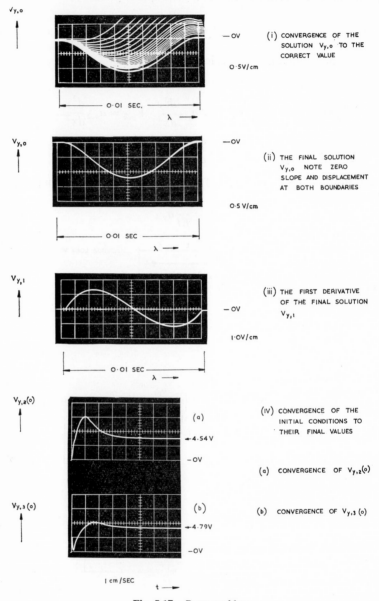

Fig. 5.17 *Beam problem*
(c) *Solution*

The computing diagram used is shown in Fig. 5.17(b) where l is represented by a repetitive computing time of 0·01 s. The amplitude scale factors used were chosen to represent a typical example of a beam configuration. Since the repetitive computing time was constant due to the fact that l is constant, M and $\overline{\text{M}}$ memories were used. The computing variables $-V_{y,0}$ and $V_{y,1}$ were tracked and the difference from zero value in each case used as a new initial condition for $-V_{y,2}$ and $V_{y,3}$ respectively. The convergence of the computing variables to their correct values are shown in Fig. 5.17(c).

The solutions of some further examples are given in Reference 12.

5.12 THE FUTURE FOR ITERATIVE OPERATION

The full utilization of the techniques will depend on the provision of fast and reliable solid state mode switching. In addition to the type of application described in this chapter other applications include adaptive control systems, general hill-climbing techniques, optimization studies and possibly the solution of partial differential equations by serial finite difference methods. The latter application, however, requires further consideration since the serial method may result in significant errors.[13] The application to function generation does not appear so attractive as the use of hybrid techniques as described in Reference 9.

REFERENCES

1. C. C. WANG: 'Solutions of Partial Integral–Differential Equations of Electron Dynamics using Analogue Computers with Storage Devices', Project Cyclone, Symposium II, April, 1952, Reeves Instrument Corporation.
2. J. ANDREWS: 'Mathematical Application of the Dynamic Storage Analogue Computer', *Proc. of Western Joint Computer Conference, I.R.E.*, 1960.
3. J. P. LANDAUER: 'Automatic Storage', E.A.I. (Electronic Associates Inc.), P.C.C.130, July, 1958.
4. M. C. GILLILAND: 'The Iterative Control System for the Electronic Differential Analyzer', Lecture delivered at I.R.E. Convention, New York, March, 1962.
5. R. K. STERN: 'The Iterative Analog', *Control Engineering*, 1961, **8**, pp. 117–21.
6. G. A. KORN: 'The Impact of Hybrid Analogue–Digital Techniques on the Analogue Computer Art', *Proc. I.R.E.*, 1962, pp. 1077–86.
7. A. S. JACKSON: *Analog Computation* (McGraw-Hill, 1960).
8. H. D. HUSKEY and G. A. KORN, *Computer Handbook* (McGraw-Hill, 1962).
9. R. J. A. PAUL and G. C. ROWLEY: 'Hybrid Computing Techniques', *Proc. of the Symposium on the Use of Computers in Mechanical Engineering*, I.Mech.E., 1963, pp. 16–25.

10. 'Dystac Analog Memory-Theory and Application, Computer Systems Inc., New Jersey, 1962.

11. J. H. MOSER, C. O. REED and H. L. SELLARS: 'Non-Linear Programming Technique for Analog Computation', *Chemical Engineering Process*, June, 1961.

12. R. J. A. PAUL, J. E. FISHER, H. B. GATLAND and A. J. MARTIN, 'An Analogue Computer with Iterative Computing Facilities', College of Aeronautics, Cranfield, Report E. & C. No. 1, June, 1964.

13. D. M. MACKAY and M. E. FISHER: *Analogue Techniques at Ultra-High Speed* (Chapman & Hall, 1962).

Chapter 6

SIMULATION OF RATIONAL TRANSFER FUNCTIONS

6.1 THE TRANSFER FUNCTION APPROACH

AS STATED IN A PREVIOUS CHAPTER IT IS OFTEN ADVANTAGEOUS to simulate the forward transfer function of non-interacting assemblies of components of a system rather than the overall differential equations of motion. In this way the engineer can identify each simulated assembly with its physical counterpart and thus a closer physical relationship exists between the simulator and the system under investigation. This method also permits the replacement of a simulated assembly by the actual components, when they are available, to confirm their operation and to give a more realistic simulation.

The simulation of the transfer functions involved is based on the use of one or more ideal computing amplifiers associated with one-terminal pair (one-port) or two-terminal pair (two-port) passive *RC* networks. The assumptions implied in this connection are discussed in Appendix A.2.

Several methods are available for simulating rational transfer functions and the basic ideas involved will now be described.

6.2 SYNTHESIS WITH INTEGRATORS AND ADDERS

The use of generalized *RC* networks usually requires special patching arrangements or the use of special computing units, and in a large machine this may be considered to be a serious disadvantage. If the necessary number of computing amplifiers required is available any rational transfer function may be synthesized by use of integrators and adders only.

Thus if we wish to simulate a generalized transfer function $G(s)$, this may be expressed as:

$$G(s) = \frac{E_2(s)}{E_1(s)} = \frac{a_m s^m + a_{m-1} s^{m-1} + \dots a_1 s + a_0}{b_n s^n + b_{n-1} s^{n-1} + \dots b_1 s + b_0} \qquad (6.1)$$

where s is the complex variable $(\sigma + j\omega)$ and the a's and b's are constants. $E_1(s)$ and $E_2(s)$ represent the Laplace Transforms of the input and output voltages respectively. m and n are positive integers where $m \leqq n$.

Now, in the equation (6.1) the values of the constants may exceed unity and as we wish to use potentiometers to give these constants it is necessary to time scale the problem as follows:

$$G(s) = \frac{E_2(s)}{E_1(s)} = \frac{A_m(sT)^m + A_{m-1}(sT)^{m-1} + \dots A_1(sT) + A_0}{(sT)^n + B_{n-1}(sT)^{n-1} + \dots B_1(sT) + B_0} \quad (6.2)$$

where T is a time constant which is an integer so chosen that the moduli of the A and B constants do not exceed unity. The new constants are given the expressions

$$a_r = A_r T^r \quad \text{for } r = 0 \dots m$$

$$b_k = B_k T^k \quad \text{for } k = 0 \dots n-1 \quad (6.3)$$

$$b_n = T^n \quad \text{(equation (6.1) is first arranged to satisfy this condition)}$$

We may write
$$\frac{E_2(s)}{E_1(s)} = \frac{E_2(s)}{E_A(s)} \frac{E_A(s)}{E_1(s)} \quad (6.4)$$

and identify the expressions for $m = n$, as

$$\frac{E_A(s)}{E_1(s)} = \frac{1}{(sT)^n + B_{n-1}(Ts)^{n-1} + \dots B_1(Ts) + B_0}$$

$$\frac{E_2(s)}{E_A(s)} = A_n(sT)^n + A_{n-1}(sT)^{n-1} + \dots A_1(sT) + A_0 \quad (6.5)$$

This gives the equation to be simulated, of the form

$$\left. \begin{array}{l} (sT)^n E_A(s) = -[-E_1(s) + (B_{n-1}(sT)^{n-1} + \dots B_1(sT) + B_0)E_A(s)] \\ \text{and } E_2(s) = (A_n(sT)^n + A_{n-1}(sT)^{n-1} + \dots A_1(sT) + A_0)E_A(s) \end{array} \right\} \quad (6.6)$$

The instrumentation of equation (6.6) is shown in Fig. 6.1. This may obviously be rearranged to take account of negative numerator constants.

This method has the advantage that very little calculation is involved in setting the coefficients of the potentiometers, which permit independent adjustment of the former.

It will be noted that for an nth order transfer function n integrators are required in addition to four adders which are required to take account of the signs of the coefficients.

For high order transfer functions the number of units required may, therefore, be excessive and the methods discussed in the following paragraphs then prove to be preferable in this respect. Before considering these further methods let us consider a typical example of this method in which time scaling is incorporated.

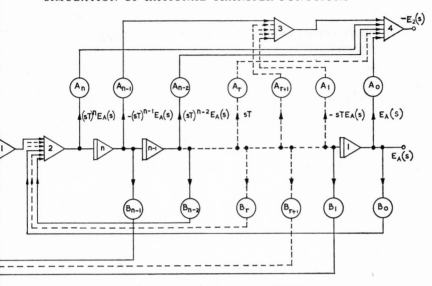

○ REPRESENTS POTENTIOMETER COEFFICIENT ▷ REPRESENTS AN INTEGRATOR

Fig. 6.1 $\dfrac{E_2(s)}{E_1(s)} = \dfrac{A_n(sT)^n + A_{n-1}(sT)^{n-1} + \dots A_1 sT + A_0}{(sT)^n + B_{n-1}(sT)^{n-1} + \dots B_1 sT + B_0}$

(Note: it is assumed that all constants are positive; coefficients of adders unity; time constant of integrators $= T$)

Example 6.1

$$G(s) = \frac{E_2(s)}{E_1(s)} = \frac{2 \times 10^5 s^5 + 4 \times 10^3 s^4 + 5 \times 10^2 s^3 + 10^2 s^2 + 2s + 5}{5 \times 10^5 s^5 + 8 \times 10^3 s^4 + 6 \times 10^2 s^3 + 50 s^2 + 10 s + 1} \quad (6.7)$$

If we select a time constant $T = 10$, then

$$
\begin{aligned}
G(s) &= \frac{E_2(s)}{E_1(s)} \\[2mm]
&= \frac{2(sT)^5 + 0 \cdot 4(sT)^4 + 0 \cdot 5(sT)^3 + (sT)^2 + 0 \cdot 2sT + 5}{5(sT)^5 + 0 \cdot 8(sT)^4 + 0 \cdot 6(sT)^3 + 0 \cdot 5(sT)^2 + sT + 1} \\[2mm]
&= \frac{0 \cdot 4(sT)^5 + 0 \cdot 08(sT)^4 + 0 \cdot 1(sT)^3 + 0 \cdot 2(sT)^2 + 0 \cdot 04 sT + 1}{(sT)^5 + 0 \cdot 16(sT)^4 + 0 \cdot 12(sT)^3 + 0 \cdot 1(sT)^2 + 0 \cdot 2sT + 0 \cdot 2}
\end{aligned}
\quad (6.8)
$$

The coefficients of the potentiometers are then given directly by the coefficients of equation (6.8)

Note: T is chosen to be a suitable integer and usually a power of 10 to ensure that all the coefficients of the expression do not exceed unity.

157

6.3 TWO-TERMINAL *RC* NETWORKS ASSOCIATED WITH ONE AMPLIFIER

The basic arrangement is shown in Fig. 6.2 together with the possible pole zero locations of the transfer function which may be realized.

If the assumptions described in Appendix A.2 are fulfilled, then

$$\frac{E_2(s)}{E_1(s)} = -\frac{Y_A(s)}{Y_B(s)} \tag{6.9}$$

where $Y_A(s)$ and $Y_B(s)$ are the admittances of A and B respectively.

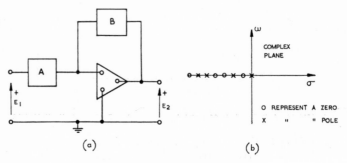

(a)   (b)

Fig. 6.2   (a) *Active network arrangement*

$$\frac{E_2(s)}{E_1(s)} = -\frac{Y_A(s)}{Y_B(s)}$$

A *and* B *represent one-port RC networks*

(b) *Possible pole-zero locations when* A *and* B *are one-port RC networks*

For a two-terminal *RC* network, in respect of the admittance function, the poles and zeros must alternate along the negative real axis of the complex frequency plane, with a zero nearest the origin.[1,6] As a result the poles and zeros of the transfer function given by equation (6.9) must also lie on the negative real axis but, since one admittance function is divided by another, two zeros or two poles may be coincident and a pole may be nearest the origin. This degree of freedom is due to the use of the ideal amplifier. Any transfer function satisfying these conditions may be expressed as,

$$G(s) = \frac{E_2(s)}{E_1(s)} = -\frac{Y_A(s)}{Y_B(s)} = -\frac{\dfrac{N(s)}{R(s)}}{\dfrac{D(s)}{R(s)}} \tag{6.10}$$

where $R(s)$ is selected so that $N(s)/R(s)$ and $D(s)/R(s)$ can be realized in the admittances of two-terminal RC networks.

The realization of Y_A and Y_B may be performed in several ways. A simple form[2] is as follows:

$$Y_A(s) = \frac{N(s)}{R(s)} = \frac{1}{R_0} + sC_0 + \sum_{j=1}^{q} \frac{sC_j}{1+sR_jC_j}$$

where
$$C_0 = \lim_{s\to\infty} \frac{1}{s}\frac{N(s)}{R(s)} \qquad \frac{1}{R_0} = \lim_{s\to 0} \frac{N(s)}{R(s)}$$

(6.11)

and q is the number of finite poles of $Y_A(s)$.

Equation (6.11) is a partial fraction expansion of $Y_A(s)/s$ multiplied by s. This expansion results in a network A comprising the parallel connection of a capacitor, a resistor and two-terminal networks each consisting of a resistor and capacitor in series. In some cases the capacitor C_0 and the resistor R_0 may not be required. The network B follows the same pattern.

To illustrate this approach consider the synthesis of two transfer functions which have wide applications in the equalization of linear servomechanisms.

Example 6.2

$$G(s) = \frac{E_2(s)}{E_1(s)} = -\frac{(1+sT_1)}{(1+sT_2)}$$

(6.12)

where T_1 and T_2 are positive constants, expressed in seconds.

We may choose $R(s) = R_0$ and thus,

$$E_2(s)\left(\frac{1+sT_2}{R_0}\right) = -E_1(s)\left(\frac{1+sT_1}{R_0}\right)$$

(6.13)

We now identify

$$Y_A(s) \text{ as } \frac{1+sT_1}{R_0} \quad \text{and} \quad Y_B(s) \text{ as } \frac{1+sT_2}{R_0}$$

Thus
$$Y_A(s) = \frac{1}{R_0} + sC_1 \quad \text{and} \quad Y_B(s) = \frac{1}{R_0} + sC_2$$

(6.14)

where
$$C_1 = \frac{T_1}{R_0} \quad \text{and} \quad C_2 = \frac{T_2}{R_0}$$

For simulator work it is often convenient to express capacitance values in microfarads and resistance values in megohms. However in some cases a different scaling factor may result in more suitable component values. The simulation of equation (6.14) is shown in Fig. 6.3.

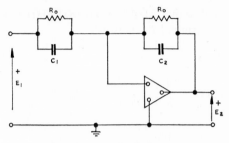

Fig. 6.3 $\dfrac{E_2(s)}{E_1(s)} = -\dfrac{1+sR_0C_1}{1+sR_0C_2} \equiv -\dfrac{1+sT_1}{1+sT_2}$

Example 6.3

$$G(s) = \frac{E_2(s)}{E_1(s)} = -\frac{(1+sT_1)(1+sbT_2)}{(1+saT_1)(1+sT_2)} \tag{6.15}$$

where a and b are positive constants which exceed unity.

The factor $(1+sT_1)/(1+saT_1)$ represents a passive phase lag and the factor, $(1+sbT_2)/(1+sT_2)$, a phase advance compensation term when the network is used to compensate the dynamic performance of a control system.

We may choose $R(s)$ to be R_0 and express equation (6.15) as

$$E_2(s)\frac{1}{R_0}\frac{1+saT_1}{1+sT_1} = -E_1(s)\frac{1}{R_0}\frac{1+sbT_2}{1+sT_2}$$

and identify

$$Y_B(s) \text{ as } \frac{1}{R_0}\frac{1+saT_1}{1+sT_1}$$

and

$$Y_A(s) \text{ as } \frac{1}{R_0}\frac{1+sbT_2}{1+sT_2} \tag{6.16}$$

Thus

$$Y_B(s) = \frac{1}{R_0} + \frac{\dfrac{sT_1}{R_0}(a-1)}{1+sT_1} = \frac{1}{R_0} + \frac{sC_1}{1+sR_1C_1}$$

$$\tag{6.17}$$

and

$$Y_A(s) = \frac{1}{R_0} + \frac{\dfrac{sT_2}{R_0}(b-1)}{1+sT_1} = \frac{1}{R_0} + \frac{sC_2}{1+sR_2C_2}$$

where

$$C_1 = \frac{T_1(a-1)}{R_0} \quad C_2 = \frac{T_2(b-1)}{R_0}$$

$$R_1 = \frac{R_0}{a-1} \quad\quad R_2 = \frac{R_0}{b-1}$$

160

The simulation of equation (6.17) is shown in Fig. 6.4.

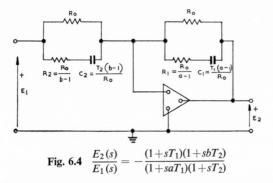

Fig. 6.4

$$\frac{E_2(s)}{E_1(s)} = -\frac{(1+sT_1)(1+sbT_2)}{(1+saT_1)(1+sT_2)}$$

6.4 TWO-TERMINAL NETWORKS ASSOCIATED WITH THREE AMPLIFIERS

With the use of one amplifier as described in the last paragraph the transfer functions which may be realized are restricted to the form in which all zeros and poles are negative real.

Transfer functions having conjugate complex poles and zeros (including the case where the zero may have positive real parts) may be realized by the addition of two sign-reversing amplifiers.[2] The basic arrangement is shown in Fig. 6.5 in which two additional passive two-terminal networks C and D are incorporated.

If Y_C and Y_D represent the admittances of networks C and D respectively then, assuming ideal amplifiers,

$$E_1(s)[Y_A(s) - Y_C(s)] = -E_2(s)[Y_B(s) - Y_D(s)]$$

i.e.

$$\frac{E_2(s)}{E_1(s)} = -\frac{Y_A(s) - Y_C(s)}{Y_B(s) - Y_D(s)} \qquad (6.18)$$

If the desired transfer function is expressed as a ratio of two polynomials $N(s)/D(s)$

$$-\frac{E_2(s)}{E_1(s)} = \frac{N(s)}{D(s)} = \frac{Y_A(s) - Y_C(s)}{Y_B(s) - Y_D(s)} \qquad (6.19)$$

The numerator and denominator may be expressed as

$$Y_A(s) - Y_C(s) = \frac{N(s)}{R(s)}$$

and

$$Y_B(s) - Y_D(s) = \frac{D(s)}{R(s)} \qquad (6.20)$$

where $R(s)$ is an arbitrary polynomial.

The factors $N(s)/R(s)$ and $D(s)/R(s)$ may be expanded in the form given by equation (6.13) and the terms resulting from this expansion divided between the pair of networks in each case according to whether the signs are positive or negative. The use of two sign-reversing amplifiers gives the

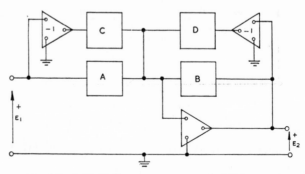

Fig. 6.5 A, B, C, D *represent two-terminal RC networks*

$$\frac{E_2(s)}{E_1(s)} = -\frac{Y_A(s) - Y_C(s)}{Y_B(s) - Y_D(s)}$$

additional freedom of permitting negative terms in the expansion and any factor $N(s)/R(s)$ may be realized provided that (i) the zeros of $R(s)$ lie on the negative real axis of the complex plane and (ii) the ratio $N(s)/R(s)$ approaches infinity no faster than s as s approaches infinity,[2,8] The same conditions apply for the factor $D(s)/R(s)$.

To illustrate the procedure we will again consider a typical example.

Example 6.4

$$\frac{E_2(s)}{E_1(s)} = G(s) = -\frac{(1+s)(1+0\cdot1s)}{(1+2s)(1+0\cdot5s)(1+0\cdot2s+0\cdot05s^2)} \qquad (6.21)$$

As $R(s)$ is any arbitrary rational function we may choose a suitable form for ease of calculation. A possible form is therefore

$$R(s) = (1+s)(1+0\cdot1s)(1+2s) \qquad (6.22)$$

Hence $\qquad Y_A(s) - Y_C(s) = \dfrac{N(s)}{R(s)} = \dfrac{1}{1+2s} = 1 - \dfrac{2s}{1+2s} \qquad (6.23)$

and $\qquad Y_B(s) - Y_D(s) = \dfrac{D(s)}{R(s)} = \dfrac{(1+0\cdot5s)(1+0\cdot2s+0\cdot05s^2)}{(1+s)(1+0\cdot1s)}$

$$= 1 + 0\cdot25 \ -s\left(\frac{0\cdot225s+0\cdot65}{(1+s)(1+0\cdot1s)}\right) \qquad (6.24)$$

By partial fraction expansion of the bracketed term we have

$$Y_B(s) - Y_D(s) = 1 + 0.25s - \frac{0.472s}{1+s} - \frac{0.178s}{1+0.1s} \qquad (6.25)$$

(Three figure accuracy)

From equations (6.23) and (6.25)

$$Y_A(s) = 1$$

$$Y_C(s) = \frac{2s}{1+2s} = \frac{sC_C}{1+sR_C C_C} \quad \text{with } C_C = 2 \quad \text{and } R_C = 1$$

$$Y_B(s) = 0.25s + 1$$

$$Y_D(s) = \frac{0.472s}{1+s} + \frac{0.178s}{1+0.1s}$$

$$= \frac{sC_D^{(1)}}{1+sR_D^{(1)} C_D^{(1)}} + \frac{sC_D^{(2)}}{1+sR_D^{(2)} C_D^{(2)}}$$

with $\qquad C_D^{(1)} = 0.472 \qquad C_D^{(2)} = 0.178$

and $\qquad R_D^{(1)} = \dfrac{1}{0.472} = 2.12 \quad R_D^{(2)} = \dfrac{0.1}{0.178} = 0.562$

Note: All capacitance values expressed in microfarads.

All resistance values expressed in megohms.

The active network arrangement for this example is given in Fig. 6.6. As illustrated by this example the calculations required to determine the

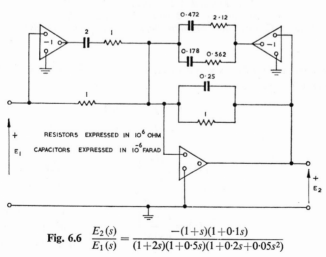

Fig. 6.6 $\quad \dfrac{E_2(s)}{E_1(s)} = \dfrac{-(1+s)(1+0.1s)}{(1+2s)(1+0.5s)(1+0.2s+0.05s^2)}$

163

element values are relatively simple, and this is obviously a significant advantage of this method. It should be noted that the range of element values is determined by the range of the terms in the expansions of $N(s)/R(s)$ and $D(s)/R(s)$. The arbitrary zeros of $R(s)$ may be chosen to control this range of values and in the general case this will result in a trial and error approach.

6.5 THREE-TERMINAL TWO-PORT NETWORKS ASSOCIATED WITH ONE AMPLIFIER

The use of three-terminal two-port networks, i.e. two-port networks each with a grounded input and output terminal, in association with an ideal computing amplifier, permits the realization of a wider class of transfer function than that obtainable with two-terminal networks.

The basic active arrangement is shown in Fig. 6.7.

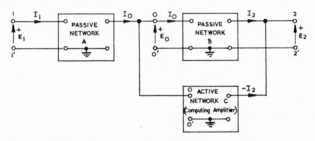

Fig. 6.7 *Basic arrangement with three-terminal networks*

Input terminals 1 1'; output terminals 2 2'
Networks A and B are passive RC networks
Network C is an ideal computing amplifier with input terminals 0 0'

Under the assumptions given in Appendix A.2, for the ideal amplifier (network C), we have

$$G(s) = \frac{E_2(s)}{E_1(s)} = \frac{y_{21}^A(s)}{y_{12}^B(s)} \tag{6.27}$$

where
$$y_{21}^A(s) = \frac{I_0(s)}{E_1(s)}\bigg|_{E_0(s)=0}$$
forward short circuit transfer admittance of network A

and
$$y_{12}^B(s) = \frac{I_0(s)}{E_2(s)}\bigg|_{E_0(s)=0}$$
minus reverse short circuit transfer admittance of network B

As described in Appendix A.2 the transfer admittance of a three-terminal two-port RC network[3] can only have negative real poles (simple and not at origin) but the zeros may be arbitrary and have any order except that they can not be positive real. From equation (6.27), $G(s)$ has poles due to the poles of $y_{21}^A(s)$ and to the zeros of $y_{12}^B(s)$. Similarly the zeros of $G(s)$ comprise the zeros of $y_{21}^A(s)$ and the poles of $y_{12}^B(s)$. Thus it may be seen that there is little theoretical restriction on the class of transfer function which may be realized by the active network arrangement given in Fig. 6.7.

There are several methods of synthesizing three-terminal networks[1,3,4,5] and a brief but good summary of typical methods is described by Truxal.[6]

The use of symmetrical lattice network transformations, as described in Appendix A.3, will be employed to illustrate the realization of a transfer function based on equation (6.27), as this approach results in relatively simple steps in the realization.

We will again consider Example 6.4 to illustrate the method.

The transfer function to be synthesized is

$$\frac{E_2(s)}{E_1(s)} = G(s) = -\frac{(1+s)(1+0{\cdot}1s)}{(1+2s)(1+0{\cdot}5s)(1+0{\cdot}2s+0{\cdot}05s^2)}$$

$$= \frac{y_{21}^A(s)}{y_{12}^B(s)} \tag{6.28}$$

We now express the transfer admittance function as

$$y_{21}^A(s) = \frac{1}{(1+2s)(1+0{\cdot}5s)} \tag{6.29}$$

$$y_{21}^B(s) = -y_{12}^B(s) = \frac{1+0{\cdot}2s+0{\cdot}05s^2}{(1+s)(1+0{\cdot}1s)} \tag{6.30}$$

These expressions conform to the physical realizability conditions for RC networks.

Network A $\qquad\qquad y_{21}^A(s) = \dfrac{1}{(1+2s)(1+0{\cdot}5s)}$

By partial fraction expansion of $(1/s)\, y_{21}^A(s)$ and multiplying the result by s we have

$$y_{21}^A(s) = s\left(\frac{1}{s}+\frac{1}{6}\frac{1}{(+0{\cdot}5s)}-\frac{8}{3}\frac{1}{(1+2s)}\right)$$

$$= 1+\frac{1}{6}\frac{s}{(1+0{\cdot}5s)}-\frac{8}{3}\frac{s}{(1+2s)}$$

165

For a symmetrical lattice network (see Appendix A.3)

$$y_{21}(s) = \frac{Y_s - Y_P}{2} \qquad (6.32)$$

where Y_s represents the admittance of the series arms and Y_P represents the admittance of the diagonal arms.

We now identify $\quad Y_s$ as $2\left(1 + \frac{1}{6}\frac{s}{(1+0\cdot5s)}\right)$

and $\qquad\qquad Y_P$ as $2\left(\frac{8}{3}\frac{s}{(1+2s)}\right)$

Hence we have the lattice network and its equivalent three-terminal, two-port network as shown in Fig. 6.8 (a).

Network B $\qquad$ (i) $y_{21}^B(s) = \dfrac{1 + 0\cdot2s + 0\cdot05s^2}{(1+s)(1+0\cdot1s)}$

$$= s\left(\frac{1}{s} - \frac{17}{18}\frac{1}{(1+s)} + \frac{4}{90}\frac{1}{(1+0\cdot1s)}\right)$$

$$= 1 - \frac{17}{18}\frac{s}{(1+s)} + \frac{4}{90}\frac{s}{(1+0\cdot1s)}$$

$$\qquad (6.33)$$

alternatively $\quad$ (ii) $y_{21}^B(s) = \dfrac{1 + \dfrac{13}{90}s}{1 + 0\cdot1s} - \dfrac{17}{18}\dfrac{s}{(1+s)}$

We again identify the series arms Y_s of the symmetrical lattice network as

$$\text{(i)} \ Y_s = 2\left(1 + \frac{4}{90}\frac{s}{(1+0\cdot1s)}\right)$$

or $\qquad\qquad$ (ii) $\dfrac{1}{Z_s} = Y_s = 2\dfrac{1 + \dfrac{13}{90}s}{(1+0\cdot1s)}$

$$\text{i.e. } Z_s = \frac{9}{26} + \frac{\dfrac{2}{13}}{1 + s\dfrac{2}{13}\dfrac{169}{180}}$$

The diagonal arms are identified as

$$Y_p = 2\left(\frac{17}{18}\frac{s}{(1+s)}\right)$$

The equivalent two-port network corresponding to lattice (i) is shown in Fig. 6.8(b) and that for lattice (ii) in Fig. 6.8(c) where the reduction is achieved by using steps (ii) and (iv) in Appendix A.3.

The active network arrangement using networks A and B is shown in Fig. 6.8(c). The three-terminal two-port B network derived from lattice (ii) is chosen in preference to that derived from lattice (i) because the spread of component values is less. In Fig. 6.8(c) the resistor values have been scaled by the factor 5×10^6 and the capacitor values by the factor $\frac{1}{5} \times 10^{-6}$

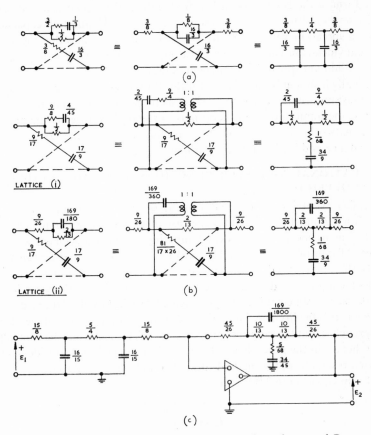

Fig. 6.8 (a) *Network* A (b) *Alternative forms for network* B
(c) *Active arrangement of network* A *and network* B *(from lattice (ii))*

$$\frac{E_2(s)}{E_1(s)} = \frac{-(1+s)(1+0\cdot1s)}{(1+2s)(1+0\cdot5s)(1+0\cdot2s+0\cdot05s^2)}$$

(Note: resistance values expressed in 10^6 ohms; capacitance values expressed in 10^{-6} farads)

to give suitable component values. It is interesting to compare the realization of the transfer function, as expressed by equations (6.21) and (6.28), by the procedures described in this section and the previous section. Referring to Fig. 6.6 we see that there are five resistors and a spread in values of about 4 to 1 and four capacitors with a spread of about 10 to 1.

These figures compare with those in Fig. 6.8 (c) where there are eight resistors with a spread in value of about 25 to 1 and four capacitors with a spread of about 12 to 1. Note, however, that if we had chosen the alternative form of the B network in Fig. 6.8 (b) the active network would comprise seven resistors with a spread in value of 153 to 1 and four capacitors with a spread in value of 85 to 1. This fact demonstrates that ingenuity pays dividends in choosing the most appropriate network configuration with minimum spread in component values.

Finally it should be noted that, for this form of active network synthesis, we must reduce the lattice network so as to give infinite shunt impedance across the input and output terminals of the derived three-terminal two-port networks since the ideal computing amplifier has zero output impedance and infinite input impedance.

6.6 RATIONAL TRANSFER FUNCTIONS WITH ADJUSTABLE COEFFICIENTS

The facility of independent adjustment of each coefficient as given in Section 6.2 may be achieved for the case of second order rational transfer functions by means of one ideal computing amplifier associated with the special forms of three-terminal T-networks.[7] High order transfer functions may then be realized by the cascade connections of such arrangements. This facility is an advantage in cases where the effect of the variation of particular parameters is to be investigated. Again in self-adaptive control systems this facility may be used to advantage. Another advantage of this approach is that the range of values of network elements may be controlled and hence, in the general case, the spread of values is not so wide as that which results from the methods described in Sections 6.3 to 6.5.

From equation (6.27) we have

$$\frac{E_2(s)}{E_1(s)} = \frac{y_{21}^A(s)}{y_{12}^B(s)}$$

If networks A and B each consist of three parallel RC networks whose short circuit transfer admittance have a common denominator $D(s)$, equation (6.27) may be expressed as

$$\frac{E_2(s)}{E_1(s)} = \frac{X_1(s)/D(s)}{X_2(s)/D(s)} = \frac{X_1(s)}{X_2(s)} \tag{6.34}$$

where $X_1(s)$ and $X_2(s)$ represent, respectively, the numerator terms of $y_{21}^A(s)$ and $y_{12}^B(s)$.

Parallel arrangements of T-networks, consisting of linear resistors and capacitors may be chosen to satisfy equation (6.34) as follows.

Parallel Arrangement of T-networks

Type 1 Standard Form

Three standard forms of T-networks are given in Table 6.1 each having a common denominator term, $(1 + ST)$, in the short circuit transfer admittance expression $y_{21}(s) = -y_{12}(s)$.

Two special cases of interest are given when (a) $N_1 = N_2 = 1$ and (b) $N_1 = 1$, $N_2 = 2$.

NETWORK	$y_{21}(s) = -y_{12}(s)$
	$$\frac{s^2 C_A^2 R_A}{1 + s2C_A R_A} = \frac{1}{2R_C}\left(\frac{R_C}{2R_A} \cdot \frac{s^2 T^2}{1+sT}\right) = \frac{1}{2R_C}\left(\frac{N_1 s^2 T^2}{1+sT}\right)$$
	$$\frac{sC_B}{1 + sC_B R_B} = \frac{1}{2R_C}\left(\frac{2R_C}{R_B} \cdot \frac{sT}{1+sT}\right) = \frac{1}{2R_C}\left(\frac{N_2 sT}{1+sT}\right)$$
	$$\frac{1}{2R_C\left(1 + \frac{sC_C R_C}{2}\right)} = \frac{1}{2R_C}\left(\frac{1}{1+sT}\right)$$
WHERE $\quad T = 2C_A R_A = C_B R_B = \dfrac{C_C R_C}{2} = CR$	
NOTE :— DENOMINATOR OF EACH FUNCTION CONTAINS $\left(1+sT\right)$	

TABLE 6.1

Case (a) $N_1 = N_2 = 1$

$$N_1 = \frac{R_C}{2R_A} = 1 \quad N_2 = \frac{2R_C}{R_B} = 1$$

$$T = C_A R_C = 2C_B R_C = \frac{C_C R_C}{2}$$

i.e.
$$C_A = 2C_B = \frac{C_C}{2} = C$$

If
$$R_C = R = \frac{R_B}{2} = 2R_A$$

$$T = CR$$

169

Case (b) $N_1 = 1$, $N_2 = 2$

$$N_1 = \frac{R_C}{2R_A} = 1 \qquad N_2 = \frac{2R_C}{R_B} = 2$$

$$T = C_A R_C = C_B R_C = \frac{C_C R_C}{2}$$

i.e.
$$C_A = C_B = \frac{C_C}{2} = C$$

If
$$R_C = R = R_B = 2R_A$$

then
$$T = CR$$

An active network is shown in Fig. 6.9 in which networks A and B of Fig. 6.7 consist of the parallel combinations of the three networks given in Table 6.1 for case (a), i.e. $N_1 = 1$.

Some possible combinations are given in Table 6.2 to illustrate the types of forward transfer functions which may be obtained. In practice, for a specific transfer function, the switches would not be required if the relevant sections only of each network were included.

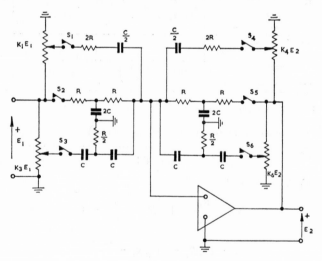

DENOTES AN OPERATIONAL AMPLIFIER

Fig. 6.9 *Active network arrangement using T-networks*
$$T = RC \qquad k's \leqq 1$$
(Assumption: output resistance of each potentiometer is negligible)

170

TABLE 6.2—EXAMPLES OF TRANSFER FUNCTIONS
GIVEN BY NETWORK IN FIG. 6.9

Network Conditions		$\dfrac{E_2(s)}{E_1(s)}$
All switches closed		$-\dfrac{1+k_1 sT+k_2 s^2 T^2}{1+k_4 sT+k_6 s^2 T^2}$
$S_1, S_2, S_4, S_5, S_6,$ closed S_3 open		$-\dfrac{1+k_1 sT}{1+k_4 sT+k_6 s^2 T^2}$
S_1, S_2, S_4, S_5 closed S_3, S_6 open		$-\dfrac{1+k_1 sT}{1+k_4 sT}$
S_3, S_5, S_6 closed S_1, S_2, S_4 open		$-\dfrac{k_2 s^2 T^2}{1+k_6 s^2 T^2}$ *
S_1, S_5, S_6 closed S_2, S_3, S_4 open		$-\dfrac{k_1 sT}{1+k_6 s^2 T^2}$ *
S_2, S_6 closed S_1, S_3, S_4, S_5 open		$-\dfrac{1}{k_6 s^2 T^2}$

* An additional amplitude limiting circuit is
required for these cases.

Such a simplified network, having many practical applications, is shown
in Fig. 6.10.

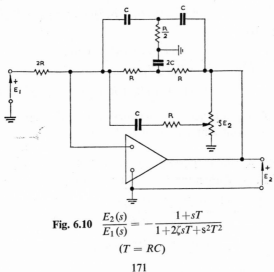

Fig. 6.10 $\dfrac{E_2(s)}{E_1(s)} = -\dfrac{1+sT}{1+2\zeta sT+s^2 T^2}$

$(T = RC)$

171

For case (b), i.e. $N_1 = 1$, $N_2 = 2$, similar combinations of the above forms of networks result in similar transfer functions except that the sT terms in the numerator and denominator are replaced by $2sT$.

Type 2 Form

A further form of T-network, which, when used in the general active network, gives a factored form of rational transfer function, is shown in Fig. 6.11.

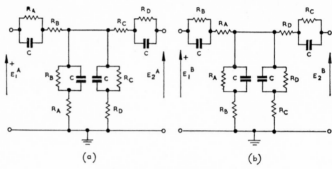

Fig. 6.11 *Other T-networks*

(a) *Network* A   (b) *Network* B

For Network A

$$y_{21}^A = \frac{(1+sCR_A)(1+sCR_D)}{[2+sC(R_A+R_B)][R_C+R_D+sCR_CR_D]+} \qquad (6.35)$$
$$+[2+sC(R_C+R_D)][R_A+R_B+sCR_AR_B]$$

For Network B

$$-y_{12}^B = y_{21}^B = \frac{(1+sCR_B)(1+sCR_C)}{[2+sC(R_A+R_B)][R_C+R_D+sCR_CR_D]+} \qquad (6.36)$$
$$+[2+sC(R_C+R_D)][R_A+R_B+sCR_AR_B]$$

The main feature of these two networks is that the denominator of the forward short circuit admittance of each network, is identical as in the previous case.

If networks A and B, having the above form, are used in the active networks of Fig. 6.7, then the forward transfer function is given by:

$$\frac{E_2(s)}{E_1(s)} = -\frac{(1+sCR_A)(1+sCR_D)}{(1+sCR_B)(1+sCR_C)} = -\frac{(1+sT_A)(1+sT_D)}{1(+sT_B)(1+sT_C)} \qquad (6.37)$$

where $T_A = CR_A$, $T_B = CR_B$, $T_C = CR_C$ and $T_D = CR_D$.

Independent adjustment of the time constants is achieved by an adjustment of the relevant set of resistors and/or capacitors.

Type 3 Form

A simplified network, which may be considered as a reduced form of T-network is shown in Fig. 6.12.

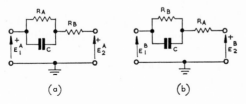

Fig. 6.12 *Simplified networks*

(a) *Network A*   (b) *Network B*

For network A

$$y_{21}^A = \frac{(1+sCR_A)}{R_A+R_B+sCR_AR_B} \tag{6.38}$$

For network B

$$-y_{12}^B = y_{21}^B = \frac{(1+sCR_B)}{R_A+R_B+sCR_AR_B} \tag{6.39}$$

The active network using this form for passive networks A and B has a forward transfer function,

$$\frac{E_2(s)}{E_1(s)} = -\frac{(1+sCR_A)}{(1+sCR_B)} = \frac{(1+sT_A)}{(1+sT_B)} \tag{6.40}$$

where $T_A = CR_A$, $T_B = CR_B$.

A particular application of this network is its use as an active 'phase advance' or 'phase lag' unit for equalization of servo-mechanisms.

An Oscillator Based on the Use of T-networks

From Table 6.2 the relevant transfer function is,

$$G(s) = \frac{k_1 sT}{1+k_6 s^2T^2}$$

If $k_1 = 1$, $k_6 = 1$, then

$$G(s) = -\frac{sT}{1+s^2T^2} = \text{say} \frac{E_2(s)}{E_1(s)} \tag{6.41}$$

If $E_1(s)$ is the transform of a step function having a magnitude V the inverse transform is given by:

$$e_2(t) = -V \sin \omega t \qquad (6.42)$$

where $$\omega = \frac{1}{T}$$

This is the equation of an oscillator.

In practice, slight changes in operating conditions and values of components result in spurious phase errors, and an amplitude control circuit is necessary.

A practical arrangement which has been investigated by the author is shown in Fig. 6.13.

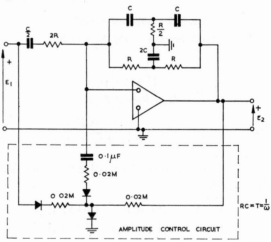

Fig. 6.13 *Amplitude-controlled oscillator*

A detailed analysis of the optimum amplitude control circuit has not been completed but results which have been obtained from the arrangement shown in Fig. 6.13 are as follows:

e_1 volts	$|e_2|$ volts
0·25	0·275
2·50	3·0
25·0	30·0

These results indicate that the non-linearity of the diodes has a greater non-linear effect on low amplitude signals than that with high amplitude values, as might be expected.

An obvious application of this circuit is its use as an amplitude controlled oscillator as used in modulated carrier systems.

Practical Considerations

The methods, so far described, suffer from two disadvantages for certain applications. The first of these is the effect of the finite output resistance of each potentiometer which is used. For applications requiring computational accuracy of better than one per cent, some circuit modifications would be necessary to compensate for this effect such as the inclusion of a cathode follower stage or the use of a graded potentiometer with a constant output resistance irrespective of the position of the wiper. The calibration of the potentiometer, in both the latter cases, must take into account the transmission factor of the modified arrangement.

The second disadvantage, particularly in cases where the networks are used in a high speed repetitive mode of operation, is the difficulty of providing the correct initial condition charges on the capacitors. Electromechanical relays may be used for this purpose but, in view of the number required, this is not an attractive solution. The use of solid state switches, in the form of silicon diode bridge networks operated by rectangular wave form switching signals, has been investigated for this purpose and initial results appear to be promising.

6.7 NETWORKS USING THE MINIMUM NUMBER OF COMPONENTS

General Remarks

The network described in Section 6.6. may be simplified if the transfer function to be simulated is one of the following forms:

$$\text{(i)} \quad G(s) = -\frac{ksT}{1+asT+bs^2T^2} \tag{6.43}$$

or $\qquad$ (ii) $\quad G(s) = -\dfrac{1}{1+asT+bs^2T^2}$ $\qquad\qquad$ (6.44)

where k, a and b are positive constants which do not require to be altered from their initial value. The time constant T may be required to be adjustable.

The reduction in the number of components is obtained by the incorporation of extra feedback paths.

Case (i), i.e. $\qquad G(s) = -\dfrac{ksT}{1+asT+bs^2T^2}$

One possible form of network, which may be arranged by suitable choice of the admittance elements to give this transfer function, is shown n Fig. 6.14.

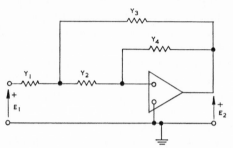

Fig. 6.14 *Network with minimum number of components* (i)

With reference to Fig. 6.14

$$\frac{E_1(s)Y_1(s)+E_2(s)Y_3(s)}{(Y_1(s)+Y_3(s))}\frac{[(Y_1(s)+Y_3(s)]Y_2(s))}{(Y_1(s)+Y_2(s)+Y_3(s))} = -E_2(s)Y_4(s)$$

i.e. $\qquad \dfrac{E_2(s)}{E_1(s)} = -\dfrac{Y_1(s)Y_2(s)}{Y_4(s)[Y_1(s)+Y_2(s)+Y_3(s)]+Y_2(s)Y_3(s)}$ $\qquad$ (6.45)

with $\qquad Y_1(s)=sC_1 \quad Y_2(s)=\dfrac{1}{R_2} \quad Y_3(s)=\dfrac{1}{R_3} \quad Y_4(s)=sC_4$

Therefore

$$G(s) = \frac{E_2(s)}{E_1(s)}$$

$$= \frac{-sC_1R_3}{1+sC_4(R_2+R_3)+s^2C_1C_4R_2R_3} \equiv \frac{-ksT}{1+asT+bs^2T^2} \quad (6.46)$$

Equating terms: $\qquad C_1R_3 = kT$

$$C_4(R_2+R_3) = aT$$

$$C_1C_4R_2R_3 = bT^2$$

$$C_4R_2 = \frac{bT}{k}$$

and
$$\frac{R_2+R_3}{R_2}=\frac{ka}{b}$$

i.e.
$$\frac{R_3}{R_2}=\frac{ka-b}{b}$$

$$\frac{C_1 R_3}{C_4 C_2}=\frac{k^2}{b}$$

$$\frac{C_1}{C_4}=\frac{k^2}{b}\frac{b}{ka-b}=\frac{k^2}{ka-b}$$

A typical example which has application in the simulation of dead-time[7] has values as follows:

$$k=2 \quad a=1 \quad b=\tfrac{1}{3}$$

i.e.
$$G(s)=-\frac{2sT}{1+sT+\dfrac{s^2 T^2}{3}} \tag{6.47}$$

Hence
$$\frac{R_3}{R_2}=\frac{2-\tfrac{1}{3}}{\tfrac{1}{3}}=5$$

$$\frac{C_1}{C_4}=\frac{4}{2-\tfrac{1}{3}}=\frac{12}{5}$$

$$C_1 R_3 = 2T = 2RC$$

If
$$R_3 = 2R$$

$$C_1 = C$$

the network to satisfy these conditions is shown in Fig. 6.15.

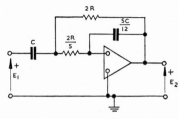

Fig. 6.15 $G(s)=\dfrac{E_2(s)}{E_1(s)}=\dfrac{-2sT}{1+sT+s^2 T^2/3}$

$$(T = RC)$$

177

Case (ii), i.e. $\qquad G(s) = -\dfrac{1}{1+asT+bs^2T^2}$

A possible arrangement to give this transfer function is shown in Fig. 6.16, where,

$$\frac{[E_1(s)Y_1(s)+E_2(s)Y_4(s)]\,Y_2(s)[Y_1(s)+Y_3(s)+Y_4(s)]}{[Y_1(s)+Y_3(s)+Y_4(s)]\,[Y_1(s)+Y_2(s)+Y_3(s)+Y_4(s)]} = -E_2(s)Y_5(s)$$

i.e. $G(s)-\dfrac{E_2(s)}{E_1(s)}$ $\qquad\qquad\qquad\qquad\qquad$ (6.48)

$$= -\frac{Y_1(s)Y_2(s)}{Y_5(s)[Y_1(s)+Y_2(s)+Y_3(s)+Y_4(s)]+Y_2(s)Y_4(s)}$$

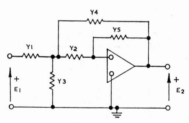

Fig. 6.16 *Network with minimum number of components* (ii)

If $\quad Y_1(s)=\dfrac{1}{R_1} \quad Y_2(s)=\dfrac{1}{R_2} \quad Y_4(s)=\dfrac{1}{R_1} \quad Y_5(s)=sC_5 \quad Y_3(s)=sC_3$

then $\qquad \dfrac{E_2(s)}{E_1(s)} = -\dfrac{1}{1+sC_5(R_1+2R_2)+s^2C_3C_5R_1R_2}$

$$= -\frac{1}{1+asT+bs^2T^2} \qquad\qquad (6.49)$$

Equating terms: $\qquad C_5(R_1+2R_2) = aT$

$$C_3C_5R_1R_2 = bT^2$$

If $\qquad\qquad\qquad\qquad 2R_2 = R_1$

then $\qquad\qquad\qquad\qquad 2C_5R_1 = aT$

$$C_3\frac{C_5R_1^2}{2} = bT^2$$

therefore
$$C_3 R_1 = \frac{4bT}{a}$$

and
$$\frac{C_5}{C_3} = \frac{aT}{2}\frac{a}{4bT} = \frac{a^2}{8b}$$

As a typical example, if $a = 1$, $b = 1$

then
$$\frac{C_5}{C_3} = \tfrac{1}{8}$$

$$\frac{R_1}{R_2} = 2$$

$$C_5 R_1 = \frac{T}{2}$$

If $T = RC$, make $R_2 = R$ and $C_1 = C/4$.
Hence $R_1 = 2R$ and $C_5 = 2C$.
The network which satisfies these conditions is shown in Fig. 6.17.

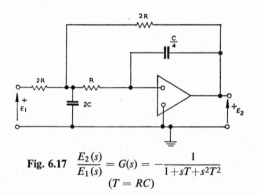

Fig. 6.17 $\dfrac{E_2(s)}{E_1(s)} = G(s) = -\dfrac{1}{1+sT+s^2T^2}$

$$(T = RC)$$

6.8 APPLICATION TO FILTER NETWORKS

The methods described in Section 6.6. may be applied to the simulation of active filters. Typical examples of the latter are the Butterworth and Chebyshev approximations of the ideal low pass filter. These two well-known approximations have particular application to statistical studies of dynamic systems. In certain applications, such as search procedures for adaptive control systems, there is a requirement for independent control of the cut-off frequency. This facility may be obtained by use of the networks described in Section 6.6. since the forward transfer function of either approximation may be expressed in quadratic factor forms.

179

For example, the fifth order ($n = 5$) Butterworth filter has a forward transfer function.[8]

$$G(sT) = \frac{1}{(1+sT)(1+0{\cdot}61804sT+s^2T^2)(1+1{\cdot}61804sT+s^2T^2)} \quad (6.50)$$

and the general expression for n odd is given by

$$G(sT) = \frac{1}{1+sT} \prod_{i=1}^{n-1} \frac{1}{1+k_i\,2sT+s^2T^2} \quad (6.51)$$

where $k_i \leqq 1$, is a constant.

For n even $\qquad G(sT) = \prod_{i=1}^{n} \frac{1}{1+k_i\,2sT+s^2T^2} \quad (6.52)$

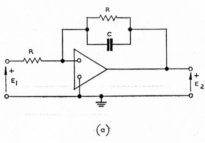

(a)

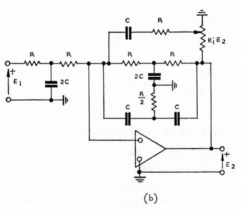

NOTE : OUTPUT
IMPEDANCE OF
POTENTIOMETER
ASSUMMED TO BE
NEGLIGIBLE.

(b)

Fig. 6.18 (a) $\dfrac{E_2(s)}{E_1(s)} = -\dfrac{1}{1+sT}$

(b) $\dfrac{E_2(s)}{E_1(s)} = -\dfrac{1}{1+k_i 2sT+s^2T^2}$

$(T = RC \qquad k_i \leqq 1)$

Thus, for n even, the Butterworth function may be synthesized by the cascade connection of quadratic factors and for n odd, the cascade connection of quadratic factors and the factor $1/(1+sT)$.

The simulation of the factors $-1/(1+sT)$ and $-1/(1+k_i 2sT+s^2T^2)$ are shown in Fig. 6.18(a) and Fig. 6.18(b) respectively.

Adjustment of T is obtained by simultaneous adjustment of all resistors or all capacitors or both. A practical arrangement would result if all resistors were in the form of precision ten turn potentiometers, used as variable resistors, and all capacitors had fixed values. This arrangement would require the use of a six gang potentiometer for each quadratic factor. If n such factors were connected in cascade, then a $6n$ gang potentiometer would be required or alternatively arrangements would have to be made to gang individual six gang potentiometers.

In view of these difficulties an arrangement of switched resistors on a decade scale may be preferable.

The general quadratic form of the forward transfer function $G(sT)$, of the nth order Chebyshev filter is given by

$$G(sT) = \prod_{i=1}^{n} \frac{1}{1+k_{i1} 2sT+k_{i2} 2s^2T^2} \tag{6.53}$$

where k_{i1} and k_{i2} are constants.

Each factor of this expression may be realized as one of the special cases of those shown in Table 6.2 with the modification that $N_1 = N_2 = 2$, as defined in Table 6.1.

6.9 REALIZATION OF FOURTH ORDER RATIONAL TRANSFER FUNCTIONS WITH ADJUSTABLE COEFFICIENTS[9]

The techniques described in Section 6.6. may be extended to give a realization of third and fourth order rational transfer functions with adjustable coefficients. Details of the method are given in Reference 9. Typical applications of such functions include the realization of adaptive filter networks in which the passband, or alternatively the cut-off frequency, may be required to be adjusted by manual or automatic means. Computing units with this facility may be used to advantage on generalized computing units and this application is described in Reference 9. The saving of amplifiers by the use of such units, or units based on the techniques of Section 6.6, may result in a significant improvement in reliability for a large computer installation comprising, say, 100 or more computing units. Experience with such large-scale computers indicates that the main source of unreliability is the computing amplifier and its associated control circuits. However, if the generalized unit is used in a repetitive computer mode, electromechanical relays or solid-state switches must be accommodated in each component network to discharge the capacitors to zero potential at the end of each repetitive cycle. This procedure is valid since the required finite initial conditions may be included in the transfer functions to be simulated. This requirement means, that to take advantage of the reduction in amplifiers, the switches must obviously be very reliable and this means solid-state switches, as discussed in Reference 9.

REFERENCES

1. E. A. GUILLEMIN: 'Synthesis of RC-networks', *J. Math. Phys.*, 1949, **28**, pp. 22–42.

2. M. V. MATHEWS and W. W. SEIFERT: 'Transfer Function Synthesis with Computer Amplifiers and Passive Networks', *Western Joint Computer Conference*, *I.R.E.*, 1955, pp. 7–12.

3. A. FIALKOW and I. GERST: 'The Transfer Function of General Two-Terminal-Pair RC Networks', *Quart. Appl. Math.*, 1952, **10**, pp. 113–27.

4. E. A. GUILLEMIN: 'A Note on the Ladder Development of RC Networks', *Proc. I.R.E.*, 1952, **40**, pp. 482–5.

5. B. J. DASHER: 'Synthesis of RC Transfer Functions as Unbalanced Two Terminal-Pair Networks', *Trans. I.R.E. Prof. Group on Circuit Theory*, 1952, PGCT1, pp. 20–34.

6. J. C. TRUXAL: *Control Systems Synthesis* (McGraw-Hill, 1955).

7. R. J. A. PAUL: 'Simulation of Rational Transfer Functions with Adjustable Coefficients', College of Aeronautics, Cranfield, Note No. 126, April 1962; *Proc. I.E.E.*, 1963, **110**, 4, pp. 671–9.

8. S. SESHU and N. BALABANIAN: *Linear Network Analysis* (Wiley, 1959).

9. R. J. A. PAUL: 'Realization of Fourth Order Rational Transfer Functions with Adjustable Coefficients', College of Aeronautics, Cranfield, Note E. & C., No. 1, June, 1963; *Proc. I.E.E.*, 1964, **111**, pp. 877–82.

Appendix A.1

THE UNILATERAL s-MULTIPLIED LAPLACE TRANSFORM

A.1.1 THE FOURIER-MELLIN THEOREM[1]

If
$$F(s) = s \int_0^\infty \varepsilon^{-st} f(t)\, dt \tag{A.1.1}$$

then
$$f(t) = \frac{1}{2\pi j} \int_{c-j\infty}^{c+j\infty} \varepsilon^{st} F(s) \frac{ds}{s} \tag{A.1.2}$$

provided (a) all singularities of $F(s)/s$ lie to the left of $c \pm j\infty$, $c > 0$

(b) $\displaystyle \int_{c-j\infty}^{c+j\infty} \left| \frac{F(s)}{s} \right| ds$ converges

(c) $\displaystyle \left| \frac{F(s)}{s} \right| \to 0$ uniformly with respect to phase s, as $(s) \to \infty$, in

the range $\dfrac{-\pi}{2} \leq \text{phase } s \leq \dfrac{\pi}{2}$. Integral is then zero for $t < 0$.

Also if
$$f(t) = \frac{1}{2\pi j} \int_{c-j\infty}^{c+j\infty} \varepsilon^{st} F(s) \frac{ds}{s} \tag{A.1.3}$$

$$F(s) = s \int_0^\infty \varepsilon^{-st} s(t)\, dt \tag{A.1.4}$$

provided (i) $f(t)$ is a continuous or a piecewise continuous function of t real > 0

(ii) Real part of s is finite and exceeds zero

(iii) Integral, equation (A.1.4) is absolutely convergent

where s is a complex variable given by $s = \sigma + j\omega$ with σ and ω real numbers and $j^2 \triangleq -1$ ($\triangleq$ means equal by definition). c is a real number such that $\displaystyle \int_0^\infty \varepsilon^{-ct} |f(t)|\, dt$ exists.

These equations constitute the Fourier-Mellin Theorem. It should be noted that attention is restricted to the positive time domain $0 \leqq t \leqq \infty$ or in other words it is assumed that $f(t)$ is zero for $t < 0$.

The function $F(s)$ is called the Laplace transform of the function $f(t)$. The latter is referred to as the inverse Laplace transform of $F(s)$.

Following the notation suggested by McLachlan,[1] we have

$$\left.\begin{array}{l} f(t) \supset F(s) \\ F(s) \subset f(t) \end{array}\right\} \tag{A.1.5}$$

Note: The Laplace transform of $f(t)$ is sometimes expressed as $F(s)/s$, i.e. $\int_0^\infty \varepsilon^{-st} f(t)\, dt$, and for this reason the relationships, equations (A.1.3) and (A.1.4), constitute the *s*-multiplied Laplace Transform Pair.

The Laplace Transformation thus transforms a certain class of function of a real variable into functions of a complex variable '*s*'. By its use, a linear integro-differential equation with a real independent time variable '*t*' is transformed into a linear algebraic equation in the complex variable '*s*'. The solution of the transformed equations as functions of *s*, when transformed back to the time domain, represents the solution of the original integro-differential equations.

As an example in the use of the above theorem consider the function

$$f(t) = \cos \omega t \quad t > 0$$

$$F(s) = s \int_0^\infty \varepsilon^{-st} \cos \omega t\, dt = \frac{s}{2} \int_0^\infty \varepsilon^{-st}(\varepsilon^{j\omega t} + \varepsilon^{-j\omega t})\, dt$$

$$= \frac{s}{2}\left[\frac{\varepsilon^{(-s+j\omega)t}}{-s+j\omega} + \frac{\varepsilon^{(-s-j\omega)t}}{-s-j\omega}\right]_0^\infty$$

$$= \frac{s}{2}\left(\frac{1}{s-j\omega} + \frac{1}{s+j\omega}\right) = \frac{s^2}{s^2+\omega^2} \tag{A.1.6}$$

The inverse transform $f(t)$ of $F(s)$ may be derived from equation (A.1.3) using Cauchy's residue theorem.[1] However, in practice it is rarely necessary to evaluate $f(t)$ in this way as a list of transform pairs is available which caters for most functions.

A few examples are given in Table A.1.1.

$$F(s) = s \int_0^\infty \varepsilon^{-st} f(t)\, dt$$

$f(t)$	$F(s)$	$f(t)$	$F(s)$
$\sin \omega t$	$s\omega/(s^2+\omega^2)$	$\varepsilon^{-at}(1-at)$	$s^2/(s+a)^2$
$\cos \omega t$	$s^2/(s^2+\omega^2)$	$\dfrac{t}{2a}\sin at$	$s^2/(s^2+a^2)^2$
$\cosh \omega t$	$s^2/(s^2-\omega^2)$	$\dfrac{1}{2a}(\sin at - at\cos at)$	$sa^2/(s^2+a^2)^2$
$\sinh \omega t$	$s\omega/(s^2-\omega^2)$	$\dfrac{1}{2a^2}\sin at \sinh at$	$s^2/(s^4+4a^4)$
ε^{-at}	$s/(s+a)$	$\dfrac{1}{2a}(\sin at \cosh at + \cos at \sinh at)$	$s^3/(s^4+4a^4)$
$\dfrac{1}{a}(1-\varepsilon^{-at})$	$1/(s+a)$	$\cos at \cosh at$	$s^4/(s^4+4a^4)$
$u_0(t)$	1	$\dfrac{1}{2a^3}(\sinh at - \sin at)$	$s/(s^4-a^4)$
$u_1(t)$	s	$\dfrac{1}{2a^2}(\cosh at - \cos at)$	$s^2/(s^4-a^4)$
$u_{-1}(t)$	s^{-1}	$\dfrac{1}{2a}(\sinh at + \sin at)$	$s^3/(s^4-a^4)$
$u_0(t-\lambda)$	$\varepsilon^{-s\lambda}$	$\tfrac{1}{2}(\cosh at + \cos at)$	$s^4/(s^4-a^4)$
$u_1(t-\lambda)$	$\varepsilon^{-s\lambda}s$	$\dfrac{1}{b^2}(1-\cos bt)$	$1/(s^2+b^2)$
$u_{-1}(t-\lambda)$	$\varepsilon^{-s\lambda}s^{-1}$	$(\cos bt - \cos at)/(a^2-b^2)$	$s^2/(s^2+b^2)(s^2+a^2)$
$\dfrac{d}{dt}f(t)$	$sF(s)-sf(0)$	$\dfrac{1}{b^2}t - \dfrac{1}{b^3}\sin bt$	$1/s(s^2+b^2)$
$\dfrac{d^2}{dt^2}f(t)$	$s^2F(s)-s\dfrac{df}{dt}(0)-s^2f(0)$	$\dfrac{1}{b^3}\sin bt - \dfrac{1}{b^2}t$	$1/s(s^2-b^2)$
$\displaystyle\int_0^t f(\lambda)\,d\lambda$	$s^{-1}F(s)$	$\cos^2 2\omega t$	$(s^2+2\omega^2)/(s^2+4\omega^2)$
$t^n/n!$	$\dfrac{1}{s^n}$ (n is a positive integer)	$(\sin \omega t)/t$	$s\ \text{arc}\tan(\omega/s)$
$1/\sqrt{\pi t}$	$s^{\frac{1}{2}}$	$\dfrac{1}{t}(\varepsilon^{-at}-\varepsilon^{-bt})$	$s \log(s+b)/(s+a)$
$2\sqrt{t}/\sqrt{\pi}$	$s^{-\frac{1}{2}}$		
$(\varepsilon^{-bt}-\varepsilon^{-at})/(a-b)$	$s/(s+a)(s+b)$		
$(a\varepsilon^{-at}-b\varepsilon^{-bt})/(a-b)$	$s^2/(s+a)(s+b)$		
$\varepsilon^{-bt}\cos at;\ a^2>0$	$s(s+b)/[(s+b)^2+a^2]$		
$\varepsilon^{-bt}\sin at;\ a^2>0$	$sa/[(s+b)^2+a^2]$		
$t\varepsilon^{-at}$	$s/(s+a)^2$		
$t^{n-1}\varepsilon^{-at}/(n-1)!$	$s/(s+a)^n$; (n positive integer)		

A.1.2 BASIC THEOREMS

A.1.2.1 The Addition Theorem

If $f_1(t) \supset F_1(s)$ $f_2(t) \supset F_2(s)$ $f_n(t) \supset F_n(s)$,

then
$$\sum_{m=1}^{n} f_m(t) \supset \sum_{m=1}^{n} F_m(s) \tag{A.1.7}$$

A.1.2.2 Exponential Multiplier

$$\varepsilon^{at} f(t) \supset \frac{s}{s-a} F(s-a) \tag{A.1.8}$$

if a is independent of s and t.

Example:
$$\cos t \supset \frac{s^2}{s^2+1}$$

$$\varepsilon^{at} \cos t \supset \frac{s}{s-a} \left[\frac{(s-a)^2}{(s-a)^2+1} \right] = \frac{s(s-a)}{(s-a)^2+1}$$

A.1.2.3 Time Scale Theorem

If
$$f(t) \supset F(s)$$

$$f(at) \supset F\left(\frac{s}{a}\right)$$

and
$$f\left(\frac{t}{a}\right) \supset F(sa) \tag{A.1.9}$$

where a is independent of s and t.

A.1.2.4 The Differentiation Theorem

If $f(t)$ and its derivatives possess transforms

$$\frac{d}{dt} f(t) \supset sF(s) - sf(0) \tag{A.1.10}$$

when $f(t) \supset F(s)$.

The theorem may be extended to include all the higher order derivatives to give the general result

$$\frac{d^n}{dt^n} f(t) \supset s^n F(s) - \sum_{r=0}^{n-1} s^{n-r} \frac{d^r f}{dt^r}(0) \tag{A.1.11}$$

where $\dfrac{d^r f}{dt^r}(0)$ represents $\dfrac{d^r f}{dt^r}$ at $t = 0$.

A.1.2.5 The Integration Theorem

If $\displaystyle\int_0^t f(\lambda)\,d\lambda \supset F_1(s)$

$$F_1(s) = s \int_0^\infty \varepsilon^{-st} \left[\int_0^t f(\lambda)\,d\lambda \right] dt$$

$$= - \int_0^\infty \left[\int_0^t f(\lambda)\,d\lambda \right] d\varepsilon^{-st}$$

$$= \left[\varepsilon^{-st} \int_0^t f(\lambda)\,d\lambda \right]_{t=0}^{t=\infty} + \int_0^\infty \varepsilon^{-st} f(t)\,dt$$

I. $\varepsilon^{-st} \displaystyle\int_0^t f(\lambda)\,d\lambda \to 0$ as $t \to \infty$ the first term vanishes at both limits.

Hence
$$\int_0^t f(\lambda)\,d\lambda \supset F_1(s) = s^{-1} F(s) \qquad (A.1.12)$$

where $F(s) \subset f(\lambda)$.
In general we find that

$$\left[\int_0^t d\lambda \right]^n f(\lambda) \supset s^{-n} F(s) \qquad (A.1.13)$$

A.1.2.6 The Shift Theorem

If $f(t) \supset F(s)$ and if λ is a positive constant

$$f(t-\lambda) \supset \varepsilon^{-s\lambda} F(s) \qquad (A.1.14)$$

i.e. translation along the positive time axis transforms into multiplication by an exponential term.

Example: $\qquad \sin \omega(t-\lambda) \supset \varepsilon^{-s\lambda} \dfrac{\omega s}{s^2 + \omega^2} \quad$ for $t > \lambda$

A.1.2.7 The Initial Value Theorem

If $f(t) \supset F(s)$
$$\lim_{t \to 0} f(t) = \lim_{s \to \infty} F(s) \qquad (A.1.15)$$

A.1.2.8 The Final Value Theorem

If $f(t) \supset F(s)$
$$\lim_{t \to \infty} f(t) = \lim_{s \to 0} F(s) \qquad (A.1.16)$$

A.1.2.9 The Convolution Theorem

If $f_1(t) \supset F_1(s)$ and $f_2(t) \supset F_2(s)$

$$\int_0^t f_1(\lambda)f_2(t-\lambda)\,d\lambda = \int_0^t f_1(t-\lambda)f_2(\lambda)\,d\lambda \supset \frac{F_1(s)F_2(s)}{s} \quad (A.1.17)$$

Many more theorems may be established and the reader is referred to References 1 and 2 for more detailed treatment, particularly with reference to technical applications.

A.1.3 THE LAPLACE TRANSFORMS OF THE SINGULARITY FUNCTIONS

The unit impulse functions, the unit step function (Heaviside unit function) and the unit ramp function belong to a set of functions called the singularity functions. Each of these functions is denoted by the symbol u_n with the suffix n denoting the power (positive or negative) of s to which the particular function transforms.

In general we have

$$\left. \begin{aligned} \int_{-\infty}^{\infty} u_{r+1}(t)\,dt = u_r(t) = \frac{d}{dt}u_{r-1}(t) \\ u_n(t) \supset s^n \end{aligned} \right\} \quad (A.1.18)$$

and

A.1.3.1 The Unit Step Function $u_0(t)$

The function $u_0(t)$ is defined as follows:

$$\left. \begin{aligned} u_0(t) &= 0 \quad \text{for } t \leqq 0 \\ u_0(t) &= 1 \quad \text{for } t > 0^+ \\ u_0(t) &\text{ is undefined in range } 0 < t < 0^+ \end{aligned} \right\} \quad (A.1.19)$$

where $t = 0^+$ is defined as the limiting value of t as t approaches the origin along the positive time axis.

$u_0(t)$ may be represented graphically as shown in Fig. A.1.1.

$$u_0(t) \supset s^0 = 1 \quad (A.1.20)$$

Example:
$$\left. \begin{aligned} \sin t\, u_0(t) &= \sin t \quad 0_+ \leqq t < \infty \\ &= 0 \end{aligned} \right\} -\infty < t < 0$$

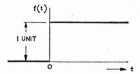

Fig. A.1.1   *Positive unit step function*

A.1.3.2   The Unit Impulse Function, $u_1(t)$

The unit impulse or Dirac function is defined as

$$
\left.
\begin{aligned}
u_1(t) &= 0 \quad \text{for } t \neq 0^+ \\
u_1(t) &= \infty \quad \text{for } t = 0^+
\end{aligned}
\right\}
\tag{A.1.21}
$$

$$
u_1(t) \supset s^1 \tag{A.1.22}
$$

Note from equation (A.1.18) that

$$
\int_{-\infty}^{\infty} u_1(t)\, dt = u_0(t)
$$

The pre-limit form of the unit impulse function, in addition to the limit form is shown in Fig. A.1.2.
Note: Only the pre-limit form is physically realizable.

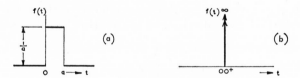

Fig. A.1.2   *Positive unit impulse function*
(a) *Pre-limit form Area = unity*   (b) *Limit form (lim of (a) $a \to 0$)*
Strength of impulse unity, i.e. infinite height and zero width

A.1.3.3   The Unit Ramp Function, $u_{-1}(t)$

$u_{-1}(t)$ is defined as

$$
\left.
\begin{aligned}
u_{-1}(t) &= 0 \quad \text{for } t \leq 0 \\
u_{-1}(t) &= t \quad \text{for } t > 0
\end{aligned}
\right\}
\tag{A.1.23}
$$

also $\qquad\qquad u_{-1}(t) \supset s^{-1}$ $\qquad\qquad\qquad$ (A.1.24)

The unit ramp function is shown graphically in Fig. A.1.3.

189

Fig. A.1.3 *Positive unit ramp function*

A.1.4 INITIAL CONDITIONS

For the one-sided Laplace transformation the assumption is made, in equation (A.1.3), that $f(t) = 0$ for $t < 0$. This means that the concept of initial conditions, that are associated with energy storage elements, must be introduced since potential and flow variables cannot be changed instantaneously unless infinite values are assumed.

The integral of a time function, which might represent the voltage across a capacitor in terms of the current flowing in the capacitor, may be expressed generally as

$$\alpha(t) = \frac{1}{\lambda_c} \int_{-\infty}^{t} \beta(\lambda)\,d\lambda \quad \text{(see Table 4.8, p. 111)} \quad \text{(A.1.25)}$$

However the integral of $\beta(t)$ from $-\infty$ to 0 is a constant and is equal to the initial condition.

If we are interested only in the solution of the equations in the range $0 < t < \infty$, the equation is modified by multiplying each term by unit step function $u_0(t)$, so that all variables are restricted to the positive time domain.

Thus
$$\alpha(t) = \frac{1}{\lambda_c} \int_0^t \beta(\lambda)\,d\lambda + \alpha(0) \quad \text{(A.1.26)}$$

where
$$\alpha(0) = \frac{1}{\lambda_c} \int_{-\infty}^{0} \beta(\lambda)\,d\lambda$$

denotes the initial condition. Also

$$\alpha(t)u_0(t) = \frac{u_0(t)}{\lambda_c} \int_0^t \beta(\lambda)\,d\lambda + u_0(t)\alpha(0)$$

$$= \frac{1}{\lambda_c} \int_{0+}^{t} \beta(\lambda)\,d\lambda + \alpha(0^+) \quad \text{(A.1.27)}$$

therefore
$$\bar{\alpha}(s) = \frac{\bar{\beta}(s)}{s\lambda_c} + \alpha(0^+) \quad \text{(A.1.28)}$$

We may also have the relationship (see Table 4.8)

$$\beta(t) = \lambda_c \frac{d}{dt}\alpha(t) \tag{A.1.29}$$

Multiplying by $u_0(t)$ we have

$$u_0(t)\beta(t) = \lambda_c u_0(t)\frac{d}{dt}\alpha(t)$$

Now
$$\frac{d}{dt}[\alpha(t)u_0(t)] = u_0(t)\frac{d}{dt}\alpha(t) + u_1(t)\alpha(t)$$

therefore
$$u_0(t)\frac{d}{dt}\alpha(t) = \frac{d}{dt}[\alpha(t)u_0(t)] - u_1(t)\alpha(t) \tag{A.1.30}$$

where $u_1(t)$ is the unit impulse function which is zero except at $t = 0^+$

therefore
$$u_0(t)\frac{d}{dt}\alpha(t) = \frac{d}{dt}[\alpha(t)u_0(t)] - u_1(t)\alpha(0^+)$$

Hence
$$u_0(t)\beta(t) = \lambda_c \frac{d}{dt}[\alpha(t)u_0(t)] - \lambda_c u_1(t)\alpha(0^+) \tag{A.1.31}$$

and
$$\bar{\beta}(s) = s\lambda_c \bar{\alpha}(s) - s\lambda_c \alpha(0^+)$$
$$= s\lambda_c \bar{\alpha}(s) - \beta(0^+) \tag{A.1.32}$$

Note that equation (A.1.32) is equivalent to the solution given in equation (A.1.10) where it is stated that

$$\frac{d}{dt}\alpha(t) \supset s\bar{\alpha}(s) - s\alpha(0)$$

Since $\alpha(0)$ is a constant, $s\alpha(0)$ must represent the Laplace transform of a unit impulse function multiplied by the constant $\alpha(0)$. Since we are dealing with continuous linear systems

$$\alpha(0^-) = \alpha(0) = \alpha(0^+) \tag{A.1.33}$$

where $\alpha(0^-)$ is defined as the limiting-value of t as it approaches the origin along the negative time axis

therefore
$$\frac{d}{dt}\alpha(t) \supset s\bar{\alpha}(s) - s\alpha(0^+)$$

A.1.5 LAPLACE TRANSFORM PAIRS

A few examples are given in Table A.1.1.

191

A.1.6   A SIMPLE EXAMPLE OF APPLICATION[1]

An *LCR* circuit is shown in Fig. A.1.4. When $t < 0$ the switch is open and C has a charge q_0.

What is the current $i(t)$ at any time after closing the switch, i.e. after $t = 0^+$?

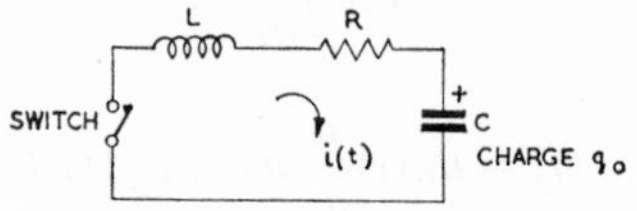

Fig. A.1.4   *RLC circuit*

The circuital differential equation may be written

$$L \frac{d}{dt} i(t) u_0(t) + R i(t) u_0(t) + \frac{1}{C} \int_0^t i(t) u_0(t) + \frac{q_0}{C} u_0(t) = 0$$

therefore

$$sL I(s) + R I(s) + \frac{I(s)}{sC} + \frac{q_0}{C} = 0$$

$$I(s) = -\frac{q_0/C}{sL + R + \dfrac{1}{sC}}$$

i.e.

$$I(s) = -\frac{s q_0}{s^2 LC + sCR + 1}$$

i.e.

$$I(s) = -\frac{s \omega_0^2 q_0}{s^2 + s\dfrac{R}{L} + \omega_0^2}$$

where $\dfrac{1}{LC} = \omega_0^2$.

Therefore

$$I(s) = -\frac{s \omega_0^2 q_0}{\left(s + \dfrac{R}{2L}\right)^2 + \omega_0^2 - \dfrac{R^2}{4L^2}}$$

$$I(s) = -\frac{s \omega_0^2 q_0}{\left(s + \dfrac{R}{2L}\right)^2 + \lambda^2}$$

for $\omega_0^2 > \dfrac{R^2}{4L^2}$ and $\lambda^2 = \omega_0^2 - \dfrac{R^2}{4L^2}$

From Table A.1.1 $i(t) = -\dfrac{\omega_0^2 q_0}{\lambda} \varepsilon^{-(R/2L)t} \sin \lambda t$

192

where the minus sign signifies the discharge of the capacitor in the opposite direction to that indicated in Fig. A.1.4.

REFERENCES

1. N. W. McLachlan: *Complex Variable Theory and Transform Calculus* (Cambridge University Press, 1955).
2. M. F. Gardner and J. L. Barnes: *Transients in Linear Systems* (Wiley, 1942).

Appendix A.2

GENERALIZED TWO-PORT NETWORKS

A.2.1 THE LINEAR, DISCRETE-ELEMENT, TIME-INVARIANT TWO-PORT NETWORK

A general form of such a network is shown in Fig. A.2.1.

A port is defined as an accessible pair of terminals.

Fig. A.2.1   *A linear two-port network*

Referring to Fig. A.2.1, terminal pair, 1 1', represents the input port and terminal pair, 2 2', represents the output port.

α_1 represents the generalized input potential variable

α_2 represents the generalized output potential variable

β_1 represents the generalized input flow variable

β_2 represents the generalized output flow variable

If the network is assumed to have no independent energy sources and all initial conditions are zero, i.e. the network is quiescent, we may describe the network characteristics by expressing the relationship between the input and output variables. In other words the network is uniquely defined by any two simultaneous equations which express the relationship between the input and output variables. Since there are four variables to be taken two at a time there are six possible sets of simultaneous equations. Before considering this topic further we will now consider the concepts of driving-point functions and transfer functions.

A.2.2 DRIVING-POINT FUNCTIONS

If we restrict our attention to a particular port, the functions expressing the relationship between the transformed potential variable and the transformed flow variable are termed driving-point functions.

194

Referring to the input port of Fig. A.2.1 we have

Driving-point impedance at the input port

$$\underset{=}{\Delta} \frac{\text{Laplace Transform of input potential variable}}{\text{Laplace Transform of input flow variable}} = \frac{\bar{\alpha}(s)}{\bar{\beta}(s)} \quad \text{(A.2.1)}$$

with zero initial conditions.

Also

Driving-point admittance at the input port

$$\underset{=}{\Delta} \frac{\bar{\beta}(s)}{\bar{\alpha}(s)} \text{ i.e. the reciprocal of the driving-point impedance} \quad \text{(A.2.2)}$$

In a similar manner we can derive these relationships for the output port.

A.2.3 TRANSFER FUNCTIONS

These functions define the relationship between a transformed variable at one port to a transformed variable at another port.

Again referring to Fig. A.2.1,

$\dfrac{\bar{\alpha}_2(s)}{\bar{\alpha}_1(s)}$ is defined as the forward potential variable transfer function

$\dfrac{\bar{\beta}_2(s)}{\bar{\beta}_1(s)}$ is defined as the forward flow variable transfer function

$\dfrac{\bar{\alpha}_1(s)}{\bar{\beta}_2(s)}$ and $\dfrac{\bar{\alpha}_2(s)}{\bar{\beta}_1(s)}$ are defined as transfer impedances

$\dfrac{\bar{\beta}_1(s)}{\bar{\alpha}_2(s)}$ and $\dfrac{\bar{\beta}_2(s)}{\bar{\alpha}_1(s)}$ are defined as transfer admittances

A.2.4 ANALYSIS OF THE TWO-PORT LINEAR NETWORK

Referring to Fig. A.2.1, we could define the network by the relationships

$$\left. \begin{array}{l} \bar{\alpha}_1(s) = a_{11}\bar{\alpha}_2(s) + a_{12}\bar{\beta}_2(s) \\ \bar{\beta}_1(s) = a_{21}\bar{\alpha}_2(s) + a_{22}\bar{\beta}_2(s) \end{array} \right\} \quad \text{(A.2.3)}$$

where the 'a' coefficients are defined as follows:

$$a_{11}(s) = \left. \frac{\bar{\alpha}_1(s)}{\bar{\alpha}_2(s)} \right|_{\bar{\beta}_2(s)=0} = \begin{array}{l} \text{reciprocal of the open-circuit forward potential} \\ \text{variable transfer function} \end{array}$$

$$a_{12}(s) = \left. \frac{\bar{\alpha}_1(s)}{\bar{\beta}_2(s)} \right|_{\bar{\alpha}_2(s)=0} = \text{forward short-circuit transfer impedance}$$

195

$$a_{21}(s) = \frac{\bar{\beta}_1(s)}{\bar{\alpha}_2(s)}\bigg|_{\bar{\beta}_2(s)=0} = \text{forward open-circuit transfer admittance}$$

$$a_{22}(s) = \frac{\bar{\beta}_1(s)}{\bar{\beta}_2(s)}\bigg|_{\bar{\alpha}_2(s)=0} = \frac{\text{reciprocal of short-circuit forward flow variable}}{\text{transfer function.}}$$

We may express equation (A.2.3) more compactly in matrix form,

i.e.
$$\begin{bmatrix} \bar{\alpha}_1(s) \\ \bar{\beta}_1(s) \end{bmatrix} = \begin{bmatrix} a_{11} & a_{12} \\ a_{21} & a_{22} \end{bmatrix}\begin{bmatrix} \bar{\alpha}_2(s) \\ \bar{\beta}_2(s) \end{bmatrix} = \begin{bmatrix} A \end{bmatrix}\begin{bmatrix} \bar{\alpha}_2(s) \\ \bar{\beta}_2(s) \end{bmatrix} \tag{A.2.4}$$

Matrix A is called the transmission matrix of the network. From equation (A.2.3) we have

$$\bar{\beta}_2(s) = \frac{1}{a_{12}}\bar{\alpha}_1(s) - \frac{a_{11}}{a_{12}}\bar{\alpha}_2(s)$$

and
$$\bar{\beta}_1(s) = a_{21}\bar{\alpha}_2(s) + a_{22}\left[\frac{1}{a_{21}}\bar{\alpha}_1(s) - \frac{a_{11}}{a_{12}}\bar{\alpha}_2(s)\right]$$

therefore
$$\bar{\beta}_1(s) = \frac{a_{22}}{a_{12}}\bar{\alpha}_1(s) + \left(\frac{a_{21}a_{12} - a_{11}a_{22}}{a_{21}}\right)\bar{\alpha}_2(s)$$

and
$$\bar{\beta}_2(s) = \frac{1}{a_{12}}\bar{\alpha}_1(s) - \frac{a_{11}}{a_{12}}\bar{\alpha}_2(s) \tag{A.2.5}$$

The coefficients in equation (A.2.5) may be recognized as admittances since they express the relationships between the flow variables and potential variables. We may, therefore, express equation (A.2.5) in the form

$$\bar{\beta}_1(s) = y_{11}\bar{\alpha}_1(s) + y_{12}\bar{\alpha}_2(s)$$

$$\bar{\beta}_2(s) = y_{21}\bar{\alpha}_1(s) + y_{22}\bar{\alpha}_2(s)$$

or
$$\begin{bmatrix} \bar{\beta}_1(s) \\ \bar{\beta}_2(s) \end{bmatrix} = \begin{bmatrix} y_{11}(s) & y_{12}(s) \\ y_{21}(s) & y_{22}(s) \end{bmatrix}\begin{bmatrix} \bar{\alpha}_1(s) \\ \bar{\alpha}_2(s) \end{bmatrix}$$

$$= [Y(s)]\begin{bmatrix} \bar{\alpha}_1(s) \\ \bar{\alpha}_2(s) \end{bmatrix}$$

The matrix Y is called the short-circuit admittance matrix for obvious reasons.

Comparing the coefficient of equations (A.2.5) and (A.2.6) we have the relationship

$$y_{11}(s) = \frac{a_{22}(s)}{a_{12}(s)} \quad y_{12}(s) = \frac{a_{21}(s)a_{12}(s) - a_{11}(s)a_{22}(s)}{a_{12}(s)} \left.\begin{array}{c} \\ \\ \\ \\ \end{array}\right\} \quad \text{(A.2.7)}$$

$$y_{21}(s) = \frac{1}{a_{12}(s)} \quad y_{22}(s) = -\frac{a_{11}(s)}{a_{12}(s)}$$

Also from equation (A.2.5) we have

$$y_{11}(s) = \frac{\bar{\beta}_1(s)}{\bar{\alpha}_1(s)}\bigg|_{\bar{\alpha}_2(s) = 0} = \text{short-circuit admittance of input port}$$

$$y_{12}(s) = \frac{\bar{\beta}_1(s)}{\bar{\alpha}_2(s)}\bigg|_{\bar{\alpha}_1(s) = 0} = \text{minus reverse short-circuit transfer admittance}$$

$$y_{21}(s) = \frac{\bar{\beta}_2(s)}{\bar{\alpha}_1(s)}\bigg|_{\bar{\alpha}_2(s) = 0} = \text{forward short-circuit transfer admittance}$$

$$y_{22}(s) = \frac{\bar{\beta}_2(s)}{\bar{\alpha}_2(s)}\bigg|_{\bar{\alpha}_1(s) = 0} = \text{minus short-circuit admittance of output port}$$

From equation (A.2.5) we may derive four further sets of relationships, i.e.

$$\begin{bmatrix} \bar{\alpha}_1(s) \\ \bar{\alpha}_2(s) \end{bmatrix} = \begin{bmatrix} z_{11} & z_{12} \\ z_{21} & z_{22} \end{bmatrix}\begin{bmatrix} \bar{\beta}_1(s) \\ \bar{\beta}_2(s) \end{bmatrix} \quad \text{impedance matrix relationship}$$

$$\begin{bmatrix} \bar{\alpha}_1(s) \\ \bar{\beta}_2(s) \end{bmatrix} = \begin{bmatrix} h_{11} & h_{12} \\ h_{21} & h_{22} \end{bmatrix}\begin{bmatrix} \bar{\beta}_1(s) \\ \bar{\alpha}_2(s) \end{bmatrix} \quad \text{hybrid parameter matrix relationship}$$

$$\begin{bmatrix} \bar{\beta}_1(s) \\ \bar{\alpha}_2(s) \end{bmatrix} = \begin{bmatrix} g_{11} & g_{12} \\ g_{21} & g_{22} \end{bmatrix}\begin{bmatrix} \bar{\alpha}_1(s) \\ \bar{\beta}_2(s) \end{bmatrix} \quad \text{hybrid parameter matrix relationship}$$

$$\begin{bmatrix} \bar{\alpha}_2(s) \\ \bar{\beta}_2(s) \end{bmatrix} = \begin{bmatrix} a'_{11} & a'_{12} \\ a'_{21} & a'_{22} \end{bmatrix}\begin{bmatrix} \bar{\alpha}_1(s) \\ \bar{\beta}_2(s) \end{bmatrix} \quad \text{inverse transmission matrix relationship}$$

For a fuller account of these relationships the reader is referred to one of the standard text-books on linear electric networks such as Seshu and Balabanian.[1] Most of the literature dealing with this topic refers specifically to electric networks where $\bar{\alpha}(s)$ is identified as $\bar{e}(s)$ (Laplace transform of voltage) and $\bar{\beta}(s)$ as $\bar{\imath}(s)$ (Laplace transform of current).

A.2.5 THE RECIPROCAL NETWORK

Up to this point the generalized network has only been restricted in the sense that it is linear, lumped and time-invariant.

If we now restrict the network to being reciprocal it may be shown[1] that the loop impedance matrix is symmetric.

This result may be established by application of the reciprocity theorem and as a result we establish the condition that

and
$$\left.\begin{array}{c} y_{12}(s) = -y_{21}(s) \\ z_{12}(s) = -z_{21}(s) \end{array}\right\} \qquad (A.2.8)$$

From equation (A.2.7) we have,

$$y_{12} = \frac{a_{21}a_{12} - a_{11}a_{22}}{a_{12}} \quad \text{and} \quad y_{21} = \frac{1}{a_{12}}$$

Using equation (A.2.8)

therefore $\qquad a_{21}a_{12} - a_{11}a_{22} = -1$

Now $\qquad \det[A] = a_{11}a_{22} - a_{12}a_{21}$

therefore $\qquad \det[A] = 1 \qquad\qquad (A.2.9)$

i.e. the determinant of the transmission matrix A of a reciprocal network is unity.

A.2.6 THE COMPUTING AMPLIFIER AS A TWO-PORT NETWORK

The computing amplifier, represented in Fig. A.2.2, is an active two-port network.

Since terminals $1'$ and $2'$ are common it may be described as a three-terminal two-port active network.

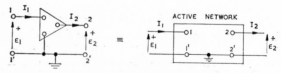

Fig. A.2.2 *The computing amplifier*

A.2.6.1 Desirable Properties of the Thermionic Amplifier

For the valve amplifier, which is in common use in most computers, we may summarize the desirable features as follows:

(i) The amplifier should be linear over a prescribed output voltage swing (commonly $\pm 100\,\text{V}$).

(ii) To avoid interaction and loading effects from coupled units the short-circuit admittance of the output port should approximate to infinity over the computing range of frequencies.

(iii) For computer use we wish the transfer function of the amplifier, when associated with feedback and input impedances, to be dictated by these impedances alone. Thus, to achieve this result, the short-circuit admittance of the input port should approximate to zero over the computing range of frequencies and leakage current, including grid input current, should be as low as possible. The effect of finite grid current is given in some detail in Reference 2.

(iv) Since negative feedback is desired in a practical computing unit, the open-circuit forward voltage transfer function should be of the form

$$\frac{1}{a_{11}(s)} = -KG(s)$$

where K is a positive constant and $G(s)$ is a rational function of 's'. Further restrictions are necessary in that $G(s)$ should contain poles and zeros which are far removed from those desired from the computing unit. In other words $1/a_{11}(s)$ should approximate to $-K$ over the computing range of frequencies. Again, as shown in the next section, K should approximate to infinity over the computing range of frequencies and typical practical values are in the range 10^7 to 10^{10}.

We have the following transmission characteristics

$$\begin{bmatrix} E(s) \\ I_1(s) \end{bmatrix} = \begin{bmatrix} a_{11}\,a_{12} \\ a_{21}\,a_{22} \end{bmatrix} \begin{bmatrix} E_2(s) \\ I_2(s) \end{bmatrix}$$

For the ideal amplifier we have from (iii) that

$$y_{11}(s) = 0 \quad \text{(over computing range of frequencies)}$$

From equation (A.2.7)

$$a_{22}(s) = a_{12}(s)\,y_{11}(s)$$

therefore $a_{22}(s) = 0$ (over computing range of frequencies)

Condition (iv) gives

$$\frac{1}{a_{11}(s)} = -K \text{ (over computing range of frequencies)}$$

Condition (ii) gives

$$y_{22}(s) = -\infty \text{ (over computing range of frequencies)}$$

From equation (A.2.7)

$$y_{22}(s) = -\frac{a_{11}(s)}{a_{12}(s)}$$

therefore

$$-\infty = -\frac{a_{11}(s)}{a_{12}(s)}$$

therefore

$$a_{12}(s) = \frac{1}{K\infty} = 0$$

Finally, because of the unilateral flow of information and zero input admittance, $a_{21}(s) = 0$.

Therefore

$$E_1(s) = -\frac{E_2(s)}{K} \tag{A.2.10}$$

A.2.6.2 The Transistor Computing Amplifier

This is essentially a current operated device as opposed to the thermionic valve amplifier which is a voltage operated device.

The basic amplifier is shown in Fig. A.2.3.

Fig. A.2.3 *Basic transistor amplifier*

For the basic amplifier we have

$$E_2(s) = -Z_T(s)I_1(s)$$

where Z_T is the transfer impedance of the amplifier.

Also

$$I_1(s) = \frac{E_1(s)}{Z_i(s)}$$

where $Z_i(s)$ is the input impedance.

Therefore
$$\frac{E_2(s)}{E_1(s)} = -\frac{Z_T(s)}{Z_i(s)} \equiv \frac{1}{a_{11}} \qquad (A.2.11)$$

where $1/a_{11}$ is the forward open-circuit voltage transfer function.

Also we have
$$E_1(s) - E_2(s) = I_1(s)[Z_i(s) + Z_T(s)] \qquad (A.2.12)$$

Thus, as far as analysis is concerned, we may represent the transistor amplifier as an equivalent ideal thermionic amplifier having zero input admittance, infinite output admittance and a forward open-circuit voltage

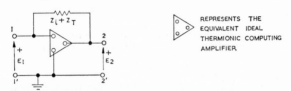

Fig. A.2.4 *Representation of transistor amplifier as an equivalent thermionic amplifier*

transfer function of $-Z_T(s)/Z_i(s)$, with an impedance of $[Z_i(s) + Z_T(s)]$ connected between output terminal 2 and input terminal 1 (as shown in Fig. A.2.4).

If we now identify $-Z_T(s)/Z_i(s)$ as $-KG(s)$ in the preceding section, then the desirable features discussed in Section 6.1 apply in this case except that the impedance $(Z_i + Z_T)$ must be taken into account.

To satisfy condition (iv) we have the requirement that $Z_T(s)/Z_i(s)$ approximates to K over the computer range of frequencies where K approaches infinity.

An additional requirement if the previous analysis is to be valid is that, over the computing range of frequencies, $Z_i + Z_T$ should be very much greater than any transfer impedance connected in parallel with the amplifier.

If these requirements can be met, and recent examples do fulfil this specification, the desirable transmission matrix of the transistor amplifier may be regarded as approximately that of the ideal thermionic amplifier in the sense discussed above.

A.2.7 THE ACTIVE TWO-PORT ARRANGEMENT (GENERALIZED COMPUTING UNIT)

The computing amplifier associated with feedback and input RC networks is the fundamental arrangement of the basic computing units of a conventional electronic analogue computer as discussed in Chapter 2. The general

FUNDAMENTAL ANALOGUE TECHNIQUES

arrangement is shown in Fig. A.2.5 where the active network C represents the computing amplifier.

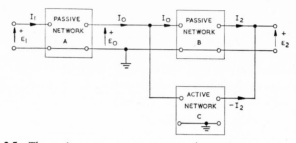

Fig. A.2.5 *The active two-port arrangement (generalized computing unit) Network C represents ideal computing amplifier*

Referring to Fig. A.2.5 we have the following relationships.

For network C

$$E_0 = a_{11}^C E_2 = -\frac{1}{KG(s)} E_2 \qquad (A.2.13)$$

(Note all quantities are functions of 's'.)

For network B

$$\left. \begin{aligned} E_0 &= a_{11}^B E_2 + a_{12}^B I_2 \\ I_0 &= a_{21}^B E_2 + a_{22}^B I_2 \end{aligned} \right\} \qquad (A.2.14)$$

For network A

$$\left. \begin{aligned} E_1 &= a_{11}^A E_0 + a_{12}^A I_0 \\ I_1 &= a_{21}^A E_0 + a_{22}^A I_0 \end{aligned} \right\} \qquad (A.2.15)$$

Substituting equation (A.2.13) into (A.2.14)

$$E_2(a_{11}^C - a_{11}^B) = a_{12}^B I_2 \qquad (A.2.16)$$

Substituting equation (A.2.13) into (A.2.15)

$$E_1 = a_{11}^A a_{11}^C E_2 + a_{12}^A I_0$$

From equation (A.2.14)

$$E_1 = a_{11}^A a_{11}^C E_2 + a_{12}^A (a_{21}^B E_2 + a_{22}^B I_2)$$

i.e.
$$E_1 = E_2(a_{11}^A a_{11}^C + a_{12}^A a_{11}^B) + a_{12}^A a_{22}^B I_2$$

202

From equation (A.2.16)

$$E_1 = E_2(a^A_{11} a^C_{11} + a^A_{12} a^B_{21}) + a^A_{12} a^B_{22} \left(\frac{a^C_{11} - a^B_{11}}{a^B_{12}} \right) E_2$$

therefore

$$\frac{E_1}{E_2} = \frac{a^C_{11}(a^A_{11} a^B_{12} + a^A_{12} a^B_{22}) + a^A_{12}(a^B_{12} a^B_{21} - a^B_{11} a^B_{22})}{a^B_{12}}$$

From equation (A.2.9)

$$a^B_{21} a^B_{12} - a^B_{11} a^B_{22} = -1$$

since network B is reciprocal.

Therefore

$$\frac{E_1}{E_2} = \frac{a^C_{11}(a^A_{11} a^B_{12} + a^A_{12} a^B_{22}) - a^A_{12}}{a^B_{12}} \qquad \text{(A.2.17)}$$

The desired result is

$$\frac{E_1}{E_2} = -\frac{a^A_{12}}{a^B_{12}} \qquad \text{(A.2.18)}$$

This means that the transfer function is determined by networks A and B above and is not a function of the amplifier characteristics, a^C_{11}, which may be subject to variation. The expression $a^C_{11}(a^A_{11} a^B_{12} + a^A_{12} a^B_{22})$ may, therefore, be regarded as an error function and to ensure that equation (A.2.18) is a valid approximation we need to impose the condition that

$$a^A_{12} \gg a^C_{11}(a^A_{11} a^B_{12} + a^A_{12} a^B_{22}) \qquad \text{(A.2.19)}$$

over the computing range of frequencies.

It is more suitable to express this condition in terms of the admittance functions since the network elements are usually specified in these terms. Thus, expressing the 'a' parameters in equation (A.2.17) in terms of the y parameters [given in equation (A.2.7)], we have the alternative form of equation (A.2.17) expressed as

$$\frac{E_1}{E_2} = \frac{y^A_{22} - y^B_{11}}{y^A_{21} KG(s)} - \frac{y^B_{21}}{y^A_{21}}$$

i.e.

$$\frac{E_1}{E_2} = \frac{y^A_{22} - y^B_{11}}{y^A_{21} KG(s)} + \frac{y^B_{12}}{y^A_{21}} \qquad \text{(A.2.20)}$$

Provided

$$y^B_{12} \gg \frac{y^A_{22} - y^B_{11}}{K} \qquad \text{(A.2.21)}$$

over the frequency range of interest

then
$$\frac{E_1}{E_2} \simeq \frac{y_{12}^B}{y_{21}^A}$$
(A.2.22)

which is the alternative form for equation (A.2.18).

Note: In the above, it is assumed that $KG(s)$ approximates to K over the frequency range of interest as discussed in Section A.2.6.

For RC networks the admittance functions are finite over a finite frequency range from zero frequency upwards. However, $y_{22}^A(s)$ or $y_{11}^B(s)$ may approach infinity as s approaches infinity and, to ensure the validity of the condition, equation (A.2.21), $y_{12}^B(s)$ should also approach infinity as s approaches infinity, if either $y_{22}^A(s)$ or $y_{11}^B(s)$ approach infinity. As described in Section A.2.6, K is desired to have as high a value as possible and the effect of a finite value of K may be derived from equation (A.2.21) and examples are given in Reference 2.

The assumptions which have been made in the derivation of equation (A.2.22) may be summarized as follows:

(i) $y_{11}^C(s) = 0$

(ii) $y_{22}^C(s) = -\infty$

(iii) $G(s) \simeq 1$

(iv) $K \to \infty$

(v) $y_{12}^B(s) \gg [y_{22}^A(s) - y_{11}^B(s)]/K$

Conditions (i) to (v) must be satisfied over the frequency range of interest. In addition we have the condition

(vi) If $y_{22}^A(s)$ or $y_{11}^B(s) \to \infty$ as $s \to \infty$ then $y_{12}^B(s)$ should tend to infinity as s tends to infinity.

A.2.8 REPRESENTATION OF NETWORK FUNCTIONS BY POLES AND ZEROS[1]

It may first be observed that, in lumped, linear, time-variant networks, the network functions are all rational functions. Secondly the coefficients in the numerator and denominator of the rational function that is a network function are all real numbers. Thus, if $F(s)$ given by

$$F(s) = \frac{a_m s^m + a_{m-1} s^{m-1} + \dots + a_1 s + a_0}{b_n s^n + b_{n-1} s^{n-1} + \dots + b_1 s + b_0}$$
(A.2.23)

is a network function, then the a's and b's are all real numbers. It therefore follows that all network functions are real on the real axis in the 's' plane where $s = \sigma + j\omega$ and σ and ω are real numbers. If a function of a complex variable 's' is real on the real axis it is called a real function. Thus the network functions, so far discussed, are real rational functions and they assume conjugate values at conjugate points in the complex plane.

A rational function is a quotient of polynomials and a polynomial can be expressed as a product of linear factors. Thus $F(s)$ may be expressed in the form

$$F(s) = \frac{A(s+z_1)(s+z_2)...(s+z_m)}{(s+p_1)(s+p_2)...(s+p_n)} \qquad (A.2.24)$$

The complex numbers, $-z_k$, for $k = 1 ... m$, are the zeros of $F(s)$ and the complex numbers $-p_1$, for $l = 1 ... n$, are the poles of $F(s)$. Thus a rational function $F(s)$ may be specified completely by giving its poles and zeros and the number A, which is merely a scale factor and may be found from the

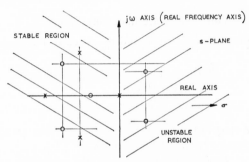

Fig. A.2.6 *Pole-zero plot of a network function*

values of the function at any point other than a pole or zero. The analytic properties of $F(s)$ are determined by its poles and zeros which are either real or occur in conjugate complex pairs. A typical pole-zero plot of a network function is shown in Fig. A.2.6 where the circle represents a zero and the cross represents a pole.

The transient response of the network is governed by the poles of the network function. As specific examples,

$$\left.\begin{array}{r} \dfrac{s}{s+p_a} \subset \varepsilon^{-p_a t} \\[3mm] \dfrac{s^2}{(s+p_a)^2} \subset t\,\varepsilon^{-p_a t} \end{array}\right\} \qquad (A.2.25)$$

and

From equation (A.2.25) we may conclude that the network function of a stable network cannot have poles in the right-half plane and any poles on the real axis must be simple (i.e. in the first degree). In other words, for our first example, if $-p_a$ is positive, i.e. in the right-half plane, the exponential will approach infinity as t approaches infinity which represents instability. Also if the poles are not simple and lie on the $j\omega$ axis or in the right-half plane instability again occurs.

A.2.9 REALIZABILITY CONDITIONS FOR RC DRIVING-POINT FUNCTIONS[3]

A.2.9.1 Driving-Point Impedance Functions $Z(s)$

(a) All poles and zeros are simple and restricted to the negative real axis in the s plane.
(b) Poles and zeros alternate along the negative real axis.
(c) Lowest critical frequency is a pole.
(d) Highest critical frequency is a zero.

A.2.9.2 Driving-Point Admittance Functions $Y(s)$

(a) All poles and zeros are simple and restricted to the negative real axis in the s plane.
(b) Poles and zeros alternate along the negative real axis.
(c) Lowest critical frequency is a zero.
(d) Highest critical frequency is a pole.

A.2.10 REALIZABILITY CONDITIONS FOR THE TRANSFER FUNCTIONS OF RC NETWORKS[3]

The discussion in Section A.2.3 indicated that the transmission characteristics of linear bilateral networks could be completely described in terms of either of two sets of three functions, i.e. z_{11}, z_{22} and z_{12} or y_{11}, y_{22} and y_{12}.

A.2.10.1 Conditions for Realizability of a Given Set of 'z' Functions of an RC Network. z Represents Open-Circuit Impedance Function

(i) z_{11} and z_{22} must satisfy the conditions for an RC driving-point impedance (given in Section A.2.9).
(ii) $z_{12}(s)$ must have only simple poles, and at each pole the residue condition must be satisfied

$$k_{11} k_{22} - k_{12}^2 \geqslant 0$$

where k_{11} is the residue of z_{11} at the pole in question, k_{22} the residue of z_{22} at the same pole and k_{12} the corresponding residue of z_{12}.
(iii) At $s = \infty$,

$$z_{11}(s) z_{22}(s) - z_{12}^2(s) \geqslant 0$$

Condition (ii) demands that all poles of z_{12} must be simple, lie on the negative real axis, and be also poles of both z_{11} and z_{22}. (Otherwise k_{11} or k_{22} is zero at one of the poles of z_{12}.) The residue condition also places a constraint on the magnitude of the multiplying factor which can be realized for $z_{12}(s)$.

The extra freedom, allowed in transfer functions compared with driving-point functions, is that there are no conditions imposed directly on the location of zeros of $z_{12}(s)$ other than the elementary restriction that these zeros must occur in conjugate complex pairs, if the numerator polynomial of z_{12} possesses only real coefficients.

A.2.10.2 Conditions for Realizability of a Given Set of 'y' Functions of an RC Network. y Represents Short-Circuit Admittance Function

Although the conditions on y_{11}, y_{22} and y_{12} for realizability by an RC network may be presented in a similar manner, the discussion is simpler if the functions considered are

$$\frac{y_{11}}{s}, \quad \frac{y_{22}}{s} \quad \text{and} \quad \frac{y_{12}}{s}$$

These three functions must satisfy exactly the same conditions as the set of impedance functions.

Thus for $\qquad z_{11}$ read $\dfrac{y_{11}}{s}$

$$z_{22} \text{ read } \frac{y_{22}}{s}$$

$$z_{12} \text{ read } \frac{y_{12}}{s}$$

REFERENCES

1. S. Seshu and N. Balabanian: *Linear Network Analysis* (Chapman & Hall, 1959).
2. R. J. A. Paul and E. L. Thomas: 'The Design and Applications of a General Purpose Analogue Computer', *J. Brit. I.R.E.*, 1957, **17**, pp. 49–73.
3. J. G. Truxal: *Control System Synthesis* (McGraw-Hill, 1955).

THE SYMMETRICAL LATTICE NETWORK

Although it is desirable in most practical problems to have an unbalanced three-terminal two-port network (i.e. one with a common ground for input and output ports), the lattice network is important as it is easier to synthesize. One approach, therefore, is to realize a given system function in the form of a lattice network and then transform the latter to an equivalent three-terminal two-port network.

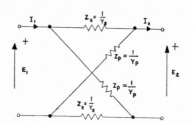

Fig. A.3.1 *Symmetrical lattice network*

Attention will be confined in this treatment to the symmetrical lattice network shown in Fig. A.3.1.

The short-circuit admittance $[y]$ for this two-port network is given by:

$$
[y] = \begin{bmatrix} y_{11} & y_{12} \\ y_{21} & y_{22} \end{bmatrix} = \begin{bmatrix} \dfrac{Y_P + Y_s}{2} & \dfrac{Y_P - Y_s}{2} \\ \dfrac{Y_s - Y_P}{2} & -\dfrac{(Y_P + Ys)}{2} \end{bmatrix} \tag{A.3.1}
$$

The open-circuit impedance matrix $[z]$ is given by:

$$
[z] = \begin{bmatrix} z_{11} & z_{12} \\ z_{21} & z_{22} \end{bmatrix} = \begin{bmatrix} \dfrac{Z_P + Z_s}{2} & \dfrac{Z_s - Z_P}{2} \\ \dfrac{Z_P - Z_s}{2} & -\dfrac{(Z_P + Z_s)}{2} \end{bmatrix} \tag{A.3.2}
$$

The problem of reducing lattice networks to unbalanced networks (without the use of ideal transformers) has not been solved for the general case. However, there is a complete solution, due to Ozaki,[1] for the reduction of the *RC* lattice network, whose network transfer functions have no zeros in the right-half of the *s*-plane, to a three-terminal two-port network.

Lewis[2] has discussed results on lattice networks whose transfer functions are restricted only in that they have no zeros on the positive real axis. This, of course, is a necessary condition on the transfer functions of a three-terminal two-port network.

Symmetrical lattice networks may be reduced to three-terminal two-port networks by the following methods.[1,2,3]

(i) *Removal of Shunt Admittance*

A shunt admittance may be removed from both Y_s and Y_P and placed in shunt at the input and output terminals (see Fig. A.3.2(a)).

(ii) *Removal of Series Impedance*

A series impedance may be removed from both Z_s and Z_P and placed in series with both the input and output terminals (see Fig. A.3.2(b)).

(iii) *Reduction of Two or More Lattices*

The lattice network may be reduced to the parallel connection at input and outpot ports of two or more sub-lattices (see Fig. A.3.2(c)).

(iv) *Removal of Shunt Admittance from Series Arms*

A shunt admittance may be removed from the series arms Y_s as shown in Fig. A.3.2(d). The ideal transformer may be removed when the remaining lattice has been reduced to a three-terminal two-port network.

(v) *Removal of Series Impedance from Diagonal Arms*

The reduction is shown in Fig. A.3.2(e) and again the ideal transformer may be removed when the remaining lattice has been reduced to a three-terminal two-port network.

The validity of the above reductions may be checked by demonstrating that the parameters of the short-circuit admittance matrix $[y]$ or the open-circuit impedance matrix $[z]$ remain invariant.

The application of the reductions is described in Chapter 6 for the realization of rational transfer functions.

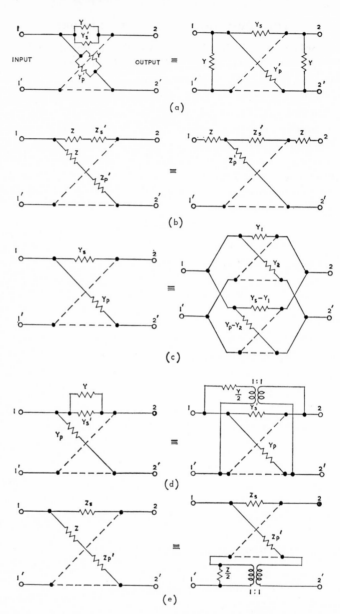

Fig. A.3.2. *Reduction of symmetrical lattice network*

(a) *Removal of shunt admittance*   (b) *Removal of series impedance*
(c) *Reduction to two or more lattices*   (d) *Removal of shunt admittance*
from series arms   (e) *Removal of series impedance from diagonal arms*

(*Note: dotted lines represent the symmetrical admittance arms*)

The reduction of a lattice network to a three-terminal two-port network for a specific case may require the application of a succession of the above methods and there is scope for ingenuity in choosing the appropriate steps.

REFERENCES

1. H. OZAKI: 'Synthesis of RC-3-Terminal Network without Ideal Transformer', Osaka Univ. Faculty Eng. Tech. Rept., 1953, **3**, pp. 57–77.

2. P. M. LEWIS: 'The Synthesis of Voltage Transfer Functions', M.I.T. Research Lab. Electronics Tech. Rept., 1956, p. 314.

3. L. WEINBERG: *Network Analysis & Synthesis* (McGraw-Hill, 1962).

INDEX